The Supermarine Swift

Airframe Detail No.4
The Supermarine Swift
A Technical Guide
by Richard A. Franks

First published in 2016 by
Valiant Wings Publishing Ltd
8 West Grove, Bedford, MK40 4BT, UK
+44 (0)1234 273434
valiant-wings@btconnect.co.uk
www.valiant-wings.co.uk

ISBN 978-0-9930908-9-9

Acknowledgements
The author would like to give a special word
of thanks to Chris at Jet Art Aviation Ltd and
Ron Fulton of the Boscombe Down Aviation
Collection for the assistance with images of the
Swifts in their care, to R. Mills for the images of
WK281 he took for me many years ago, and to
Richard J, Caruana for his superb artwork.

Note
There are many different ways of writing aircraft designation, however the Swift operated
in the post-1948 period when the RAF adopted
the Arabic system of numbering (e.g. F Mk 6),
so we will use this system throughout this title.

Swift F4 Silhouette

Sections

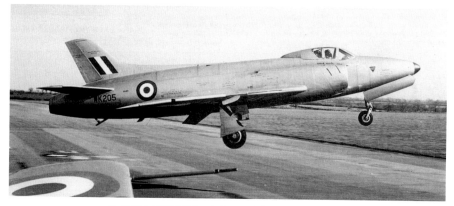

Swift F Mk 1 WK205 just before touchdown (©Air Ministry/MOD)

Glossary

A&AEE ..... Aircraft & Armament Experimental
             Establishment, Boscombe Down
AFDS .... Air Fighting Development Squadron,
             West Raynham
C(A) .... Controller (Aircraft)
CO .... Commanding Officer
ETPS .... Empire Test Pilot's School, Farnborough
Flt .... Flight
ft .... Foot
GP .... General Purpose
GWDS ...... Guided Weapons Development
             Squadron, Valley
HQ .... Headquarters
IFF .... Identification Friend or Foe
Imp. Gal. .. Imperial Gallon

in .... Inch
lb .... Pound
Mk .... Mark
Mod .... Modification
mph .... Miles Per Hour
MU .... Maintenance Unit (RAF)
No .... Number
PO .... Petty Officer
RAE .... Royal Aircraft Establishment
RAF .... Royal Air Force
R.P. .... Rocket Projectile
SOC .... Struck Off Charge
SofTT .... School of Technical Training
Sqn .... Squadron
UK .... United Kingdom

The Type 510 VV106 seen in flight in the original configuration with the rounded nose cone (©Ministry of Supply)

Introduction

Brief History

Chief Designer Joe Smith and test pilot Mike Lithgow stand in front of VV119 (©Vickers)

Swept-wing Attacker

Towards the end of WWII and in the immediate post-war era, British aviation development became stagnant. Little was done to develop new types, nor to take notice of, or use, captured Third Reich research into swept-wing design. Britain fell behind America and Russia, but by 1946 the Air Staff realised that it was behind with the development and procurement of high-speed aircraft and as a result issued specifications for a bomber and single- and two-seat fighters. Issued in January 1947 specification F.43/46 was for a new RAF day interceptor and a number of firms submitted various designs. Within a year the Specification was outdated, due to the rapid evolution in aerodynamics and aircraft designs of this era, so a new Specfication (F.3/48) was issued in early 1948. The powers-that-be decided that the best option to meet this specification was Hawker's P.1067 (later to become the Hunter) and so effectively wrote the specification around the type. The Supermarine division of Vickers-Armstrong had submitted their Type 526 to F.3/48, but it was not selected. At this time they were also working on a swept-wing development of the Attacker (See Supermarine Attacker - The Navy's first jet fighter, by this author ISBN: 978-1-905414-05-6). Two prototypes were ordered by the Ministry of Supply and these were allocated serial numbers VV106 and VV119. Each featured the Attacker fuselage complete with its tailwheel configuration, but both the wings and tailplanes were swept back at 40 degrees. Powered by a Rolls-Royce Nene 2 engine, the design was envisaged to achieve a maximum speed of 700mph. The type was also to be fitted with a variable-incidence tailplane with a quarter-chord elevator without horn balances or tabs (all photos show both VV106 and VV119 had horn-balanced elevators and the lack of any gap around the root of each tailplane seems to rule out the actual fitment of a variable-incidence [trimable] unit). The first machine, designated the Type 510 (VV106), took to the air from A&AEE Boscombe Down, Wiltshire, on the 29th December 1948 with Supermarine's Chief Test Pilot Mike Lithgow at the controls. The test programme with this machine was terminated after a wheels-up landing on the 16th March 1949, but resumed on the 10th May after the airframe was repaired. Speeds of up to Mach 0.9 were easily achieved, with an average of 630-635mph within the 10,000ft to 15,000ft range. The maximum speed of Mach 0.93 was identified as being the point at which a change in lateral trim occurred (dropping the port wing), and full starboard movement of the control column was required to correct this. This maximum speed at last saw a type that could exceed the Mach 0.92 limit of the Spitfire.

The Type 510 was demonstrated to the public at the SBAC event at Farnborough between the 6th and 11th September 1949 and it was well received during the six flights undertaken at the show. It then undertook handling trials at A&AEE Boscombe Down during the remainder of September and through into November. These quickly identified that the swept wings limited the useable lift coefficient in the transonic region while considerably increasing the lift at high speeds. Wg Cdr Peter Wykham-Barnes DSO, OBE, DFC, the CO of A Squadron at Boscombe Down flew the aircraft on the 21st October 1949 in response to comments from his pilots that it was showing worsening symptoms of vibration. At power settings of two-thirds and above the aircraft handled well, but when the engine was throttled-back severe vibration set in and the nose jerked 5 degrees either side of the flight path. A long, low approach with high rpm was required to recover the aircraft and extreme care was needed during the landing approach as a result. Manoeuvrability was also hampered by the longitudinal instability inherent in the swept wing when nearing the stall, and a lack of power from the Nene engine also reduced turning performance in level flight. These factors all combined to mean that at 40,000ft the type was basically restricted to straight and level flight. The test pilots found the type had an excellent rate of roll at low level and it did not seem to exhibit any of the tendencies everyone had foretold for swept-wing designs, such as snaking or Dutch Rolls. The test pilots did not like the tailwheel configuration though and felt that a tricycle undercarriage combined with improved elevator controls would make the type into a good fighter. Testing was delayed by a wheels-up landing by Mike Lithgow on the 29th December 1949 after an engine failure that was thought to have been caused by similar vibrations. It was not until the 10th May 1950 that the repaired aircraft was able

A nice head-on shot of the Type 510 (VV106) in flight in its original configuration during a PR air-to-air photographic sortie with C.E. Brown for the Air Ministry/Ministry of Supply *(©C.E. Brown)*

to resume testing and by this time the name Swift had been bestowed on the design. The vibrations associated with throttling back the engine were found to be caused by turbulence in the air intakes and this was cured by fitting a modified Attacker-type front engine mount combined with modifications to the boundary layer bleeds in the air intake ducts. Comparison trials with the North American F-86A Sabre did show that the type was inferior at low level, but at 25,000ft the two were almost level, with the Type 510 achieving 617mph to the Sabre's 619.5mph. Much of the superiority of the Sabre was down to its standard of finish and its more powerful engine combined with a better air intake system. It should be remembered that the Type 510 was basically a conversion of the Attacker and was meant purely to investigate the swept-wing concept rather than to act as a prototype of a proposed production design.

During mid-1950 the type was modified for naval trials, and in this configuration was first

flown by Mike Lithgow on the 14th September 1950. The aircraft was then delivered by Les Colquhoun to RAE Farnborough on the 20th September. These tests, which were designed to see if a swept-wing type could be operated from a carrier, initially consisted of dummy deck landings as well as rocket-assisted take-offs. The type was found to handle well even with four rocket bottles and on the 8th November 1950 it became the first swept-wing aircraft to land and take off from a carrier. Piloted by Lt J. Elliott (RN) and assisted by Lt Cdr D G Parker and Mike Lithgow, twelve landings and rocket-assisted takes-offs were achieved from HMS Illustrious. Take-off was achieved in about 500ft, with the carrier into wind at about 22-25 knots and with two RATO bottles fitted to VV106. Landing approach was between 124-134 knots indicated, and the undercarriage reacted very well to the rigours of a deck landing. Handling on the deck, along with refuelling and re-arming was all found to be good and the type only returned to base later that day because a fuel pressure warning light refused to go out. The final take-off on the 14th November was to prove the most eventful, however, as one of the rockets did not give the same thrust as the other, making the aircraft swing and the wing tip struck the carrier's port gun turret, causing considerable damage to both aircraft and turret. Thankfully the pilot, Lt Cdr Parker, was sufficiently skilled to cope with this situation, completed the take-off and returned the precious prototype safely to Boscombe Down. As the first production Attacker was undertaking similar trials on HMS Illustrious at the same time, this gave the manufacturer and the Royal Navy, a good chance to compare the interim Attacker with the potential of a swept-wing design.

After repair VV106 returned to RAE

The Type 510 (VV106) makes the first landing on a swept-wing jet aircraft on an aircraft carrier, when it landed on HMS Illustrious on the 17th November 1950 *(©British Official)*

The Type 510 (VV106) comes in to land at Farnborough, showing off the revised elongated nose profile to good effect (©Ministry of Supply)

Farnborough for further high-speed research before returning to Supermarine for the removal of all the naval equipment. The type was to have one more modification, though, when, in response to the December 1948 proposal to fit a fully adjustable tailplane, the type was fitted with a revised rear fuselage designed by Tiltman Langley Laboratories that pivoted and was driven by a trimming screwjack to adjust the incidence through 4 degrees up and down. Fitted with the variable-incidence tail (thus becoming the Type 517), VV106 was found to be very stable and the previous Mach 0.95 limit was relaxed considerably thereafter. In this configuration VV106 suffered a wheels-up landing at RAE Farnborough following undercarriage failure on the 14th November 1952 with T. Gordon Innes at the controls. After repairs the aircraft was flown once again by Dave Morgan

on the 2nd September 1953.

VV106 ended its flying career on the 14th January 1955 when it was allocated to the RAF School of Technical Training at Melksham. The aircraft later moved to Halton, before spending some time as a gate guardian at RAF Cardington behind the main HQ building (built by Short Bros.). It then moved as an exhibit to the museum at RAF Colerne and then into the collection of the RAF Museum, who stored it at Cosford before it was loaned to the FAA Museum at RNAS Yeovilton, where it remains today in storage within the Cobham Hall reserve collection facility.

Type 525-535

The second prototype, VV119, was essentially similar to VV106 but had been modified in step with the development of the Type 510, so was designated the Type 525. It first flew

from A&AEE Boscombe Down with Mike Lithgow at the controls on the 27th March 1950. The type did not undertake much testing though in this form and was grounded for modification by Supermarine at the beginning of May 1950. When it re-emerged it featured a forward-retracting nose wheel undercarriage (although it still retained the tailwheels), the main undercarriage oleos were moved aft, it had a larger rear fuselage to accommodate a larger jet pipe with primitive reheat, revised longer nose cone and air intakes, provision for wing-mounted guns (the planned four 20mm cannon were never fitted although four dummy gun fairings were installed for the SBAC event at Farnborough that year) that thus reduced the span of the ailerons, the 'bubble' canopy reverted to a more conventional framed version, no anti-spin parachute or housing was fitted and an improved fuel system resulted in better fuel efficiency and greater fuel capacity. In this guise VV119 was designated the Type 535 and had the wing roots extended both forwards and aft, thus increasing and decreasing the inboard sweep of the leading and trailing edges. In this form the type first flew on the 23rd August 1950 from A&AEE Boscombe Down, with the reheat system being used in flight for the first time on the 1st September. This system was crude in comparison to other nations' systems, as the UK had been very slow in adopting afterburner, so the crude jet pipe just had a two-position twin-eyelid nozzle. It immediately went to Farnborough to attend that year's SBAC event and exhibited excellent handling with none of the elevator buffeting experienced with the previous Type 510 or 525. The type did suffer with directional instability, though, caused by the lengthened nose, so it was modified once again by the addition of a dorsal fin fillet. Operation with the 535 from Chilbolton was marginal at best, as the type needed 3,000ft of runway to get airborne. Also, if the eyelids opened without full afterburner thrust, the

A superb image of the Type 535 (VV119) in flight (©Vickers)

power dropped instantly from 6,800lb of thrust to just 4,000lb! Wing fences were installed on VV119 and it flew for the first time with them on the 28th December. Supermarine designed a 250 Gallon drop tank for the 535, but it was never used as the Air Staff thinking of the period was that endurance and long range were not important. This was just as well, as apparently with the drop tank the type would have had difficulty in taking off even from the huge runway at A&AEE Boscombe Down. Much of the thinking of the Air Staff was simply down to a naive attitude and the wish to continue using types like the Meteor and Vampire along with their fuel-efficient Nene engines, instead of the far more fuel-hungry co-axial engines like the Avon. Test flying of VV19 was taken over by Sqn Ldr Dave W Morgan from October 1951 and alongside others he undertook flying this machine for the starring role in the feature film Sound Barrier, where VV119 carried the name Prometheus. Further tests using VV119 included anti-gravity flight clothing and drag-inducing upper surface flaps, the latter proving to cause buffeting and were deemed unnecessary, as the landing flaps were effective to reduce speed. A system was installed, operated by a switch on the throttle lever, that set the flaps at either 35 or 55 degrees and this allowed at low altitude the top speed to be reduced to 160 knots in 58 seconds, or a glide of 25,000ft/min to be achieved from 40,000ft without exceeding Mach 0.79. In 1955 the wings of VV119 were modified to take various combinations of dummy Blue Sky rockets, to ascertain how these affected speed, manoeuvrability and

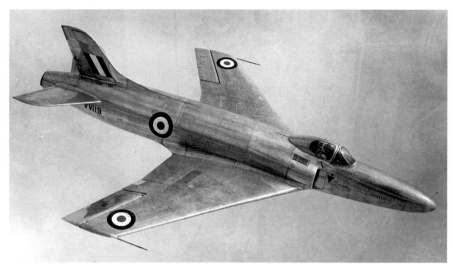

VV119 marked as Prometheus for the David Lean film, Sound Barrier (©Vickers)

The first pre-production Swift was Type 541 WJ960, seen here in flight from Chilbolton (©Vickers)

Old and new as the Type 541 (WJ960) flies alongside Spitfire PK524, which was used by Vickers-Supermarine as a chase plane (©Vickers)

The second pre-production Swift was more like the actual F Mk 1 and it (WJ965) can be seen in this official image of the type on the taxiway at South Marston (©Ministry of Supply)

handling. Speeds up to Mach 0.95 with two and 0.90 with four rockets were achieved and although no adverse effects were noted in general handling, greater inertia during rolls was inevitable.

It is probably worth noting that when a team led by Dave Morgan visited the first F-86s to be based in the UK at North Luffenham they were amazed to see the quality of the aircraft, along with the advanced nature of such things as access panel fixtures and the canopy. At this time the UK aircraft industry could not make a blown Plexiglas canopy like that of the F-86 and all access panels etc. on British aircraft were attached with a multitude of screws, not quick-release fasteners. Morgan commented that the cockpit was "like something out of the 21st century, whereas that of the 535 was much like that of the Spitfire". This probably tells you all you need to know about how behind Britain had become in the aeronautical sphere during the immediate post-war period.

VV119's flying career ended in September 1955 when it was sent to RAF Halton and allocated Instructional Airframe No.7285M, and it is presumed that it was eventually scrapped there.

Birth of the Swift

On 9th November 1950 the Air Ministry ordered two pre-production Type 541s along with 100 production airframes, all fitted with the Rolls-Royce RA7 Avon engine against Specification F.105P. Many consider the Type 541 to be the prototype Swift but Dave Morgan stated that this was not the case, as although they featured the enlarged fuselage to take the Avon engine, the space for extra fuel tanks was left empty, with the fuselage tank capacity thus remaining 360 Gallons. These two pre-production machines were given serial numbers WJ960 and WJ965 and were respectively known as Swift F Mk 1 Pro-

totype 1 and 2. Whilst WJ960 was very much still a prototype, WJ965 was intended to be more representative of the production Swift, and was to be built to production standard with all operational equipment installed (it was thus a true pre-production airframe). Development and adoption of the type had been accelerated by the Korean War, which had required the Air Ministry to procure the Swift as a fighter back-up should the Hawker Hunter then under development prove to be unsuccessful.

The first prototype, WJ960, was basically similar to VV119 with the exception of the Rolls-Royce Avon engine that offered nearly 50% more power than the Nene and the increased aileron span due to the absence of wing-mounted guns. It was moved by road for its first flight from A&AEE Boscombe Down on the 1st August 1951 and various control oscillations were encountered. During the third flight on the 3rd August for a photographic session, Mike Lithgow experienced severe control vibrations caused by mechanical rather than aerodynamic problems, These vibrations, caused by aileron flutter, caused a fuel cock linkage to break thus shutting down the engine, Mike Lithgow was able to make a very skilled power-off landing at Chilbolton, thus preserving the precious aircraft. By the 5th September it was obvious that elevator control was not good during turns, especially over 4.5g. WJ960 suffered another engine failure on the 8th September, while Dave Morgan was practicing for that year's SBAC event, and once again made a forced landing at Charity Down Farm. The failure occurred at 800ft on the approach to land and because of the hazard the River Test represented in its step-sided valley some 400ft from the runway threshold, he was forced to retract the undercarriage and turn downwind to land in less dangerous terrain. This time the airframe sustained heavy damage to the tail, the starboard wing struck a tree and the port a brick structure (actually an outside lavatory, but it was not occupied at the time). The pilot

A superb shot of the second Type 541 (WJ965) in flight, showing off the original wing shape (©Ministry of Supply)

was shaken but otherwise uninjured and despite the damage WJ960 was repaired and flying again by December. As a footnote to this, when Dave Morgan MBE passed away on the 3rd February 2004, he asked that his ashes be scattered on Chilbolton airfield, which by this stage was part of a farming estate that included Charity Down Farm. On the 11th July 1952 Dave Morgan flew WJ960 to Brussels for exhibition and in so doing set a point-to-point record with an average speed of 665.9mph and a flight time of 18 minutes and 3.3 seconds. Still retaining the fixed tail, WJ960 was temporarily grounded to have a variable-incidence tail and geared aileron tabs fitted and it flew in this configuration on the 4th February 1953. Mach 0.91 was achieved before aileron flutter was experienced but this was quickly overcome by the application of the air brakes. A service pilot had discovered that the engine was prone to surge when the aircraft was being flown near to the stall at high altitude when there was a very low ambient temperature and the engine would also flame out when the guns were fired. Production F Mk 1 WK203 was allocated to Rolls-Royce in February 1954 to assist with research into these phenomena and for a while WJ960 attempted to simulate engine surge but only managed to do this in three out of ten flights. Once these tests were completed, it moved to RAE Bedford for arrester barrier trials and having sustained damage there during these trials it was withdrawn from use on the 15th September 1959 and subsequently sold as scrap.

WJ965, the second pre-production prototype, was first flown by Dave Morgan on the 18th July 1952 (some state the 14th) from A&AEE Boscombe Down. It was more representative of the production machines and featured a modified nose, canopy and the 1ft taller vertical fin. Wing position in relation to the fuselage was revised and the wingtips, like WJ960, had the Kuchemann curve. Wing and aileron flutter were experienced during flight testing, far worse than with WJ960, and this was a combination of the use of spring-tab ailerons and the reduction in the thickness of the wing skinning that had been undertaken in an attempt to reduce the overall weight of

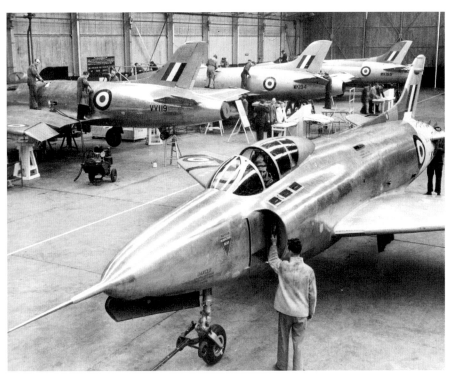

The second Swift F Mk 1 WK965 is seen here at Hursley Park in 1952 with VV119 and pre-production Swifts WK194 and 195 (©Vickers)

the type. On the 18th July it flew to the Chilbolton airfield to begin manufacturer's trials. During this flight, undertaken by Dave Morgan, he discovered that at 270 knots (311mph) snaking set in accompanied by sympathetic movement of the rudder and if the speed was increased to 300 knots (345mph) it got worse. The effect could be reduced by gentle pressure on the rudder pedals, but if the pilot did not do this, the snaking increased. It was only when the anti-spin parachute was removed on the 22nd July that this snaking ceased and speeds up to 450 knots (518mph) could be achieved. In a flight on the 22nd July Les Calquhoun found that the ailerons were much heavier in their operation than those on VV119. This got worse with altitude and above Mach 0.88 they were extremely heavy. Dives up to Mach 0.93 were undertaken and nose-down trim change was noted at Mach 0.86-0.87, although the amount of control column movement to correct this increased with speed. Level flight top speed was Mach 0.89 and this was registered during the seventh flight on the 27th July. Fol-

lowing the loss of the D.H.110 (See Sea Vixen - De Havilland's Ultimate Fighter Aircraft by the same author, ISBN: 1-905414-04-8) in September 1952, WJ965 was grounded while additional structural test equipment and high-speed cameras to film the wings and ailerons could be fitted prior to an intensive new test programme. It took to the air again on the 22nd November, and within a couple of weeks the results had been fully analysed. The tests resulted in an interim measure of replacing the spring-tabs with geared examples and once these were installed the Swift became the first Supermarine type to exceed the speed of sound. This occurred, much to the delight of Chilbolton staff, on the 26th February 1953, although Dave Morgan had experienced all signs of supersonic flight in his previous dive on the 24th. Sadly WJ965 was lost, along with its pilot Sqn Ldr Noel E D Lewis of A Squadron A&AEE, on the 10th November 1953. Sqn Ldr Lewis was the new project pilot for the Swift in pursuance of the C(A) release for the type and had been undertaking power-on and -off stalls in both clean (wheels, flaps up) and dirty (wheels and flaps down) configurations above 15,000ft. Twenty-five minutes after take-off the aircraft was seen to be flying slowly at 5,000ft, then the engine noise decreased and the aircraft entered a flat spin. It struck the ground after three and a half turns and although the pilot and seat were ejected from the aircraft, this happened on impact. Subsequent research was hampered by the fact that all flight data was destroyed in the fire that followed impact, but from the notes on the pilot's kneepad it was agreed that the accident had occurred after the second (dirty) stall with power on. Nothing was found to be wrong with the aircraft systems and the pilot had

This is the first production Swift F Mk 1, WK194, seen taxiing in after a flight, probably at Farnborough

Swift F Mk 1s WK205, WK206, WK211 and WK212 on their way from South Marston to AFDS West Raynham on the 13th February 1954 (©Vickers)

been fit, so it was later deduced having looked at the stall reports made by Jock Elliot RN with VV106 back in 1950, that the type would show a marked reluctance to recover from a stall without the use of power from a very early stage. It was therefore thought that Sqn Ldr Lewis had simply continued to attempt stall recovery beyond the point of no return.

Into production

F Mk 1

The first production Swift F Mk 1 from the initial batch was WK194 and it made its maiden flight on the 25th August 1952. Along with WK195, it was built by the experimental shop at Hursley Park, while all subsequent machines were built at South Marston. The type was armed with two 30mm Aden cannon, had a fixed tailplane and an Avon 108 engine without afterburner. The first true production Swift was WK196, which was similar to the two previous pre-production prototypes. In March 1952 the government introduced the Superpriority Scheme, whereby certain new types were given priority for production, manpower and material and as a result the Swift order was doubled, with the extras due to be manufactured by Short & Harland at Belfast.

WK194 was tested by Sqn Ldr Christopher G Clark DFC of A Squadron, A&AEE, who flew it at Chilbolton on the 8th November 1952. This was the first time a service test pilot had flown the type and his report was disturbing, as it highlighted numerous problems with the design. He undertook two flights and reported that the aircraft was unstable prior to the stall, it tightened in turns (pitch-up) with no input from the pilot, the wing dropped dramatically at the stall and the oscillation of the ailerons increased with speed. As a result of these findings A&AEE asked the Ministry of Supply to allow

them to undertake flight trials with the Swift before any agreed trials programme was started. Agreement was not given however as Supermarine were already well aware of the shortcomings of the design and had set in motion a series of modifications to overcome them. As mentioned previously, these modifications included the planned installation of a variable-incidence tailplane, wing fences and fully-powered ailerons

On the 1st October 1953 the CO of the AFDS (Air Fighting Development Squadron) of the CFE (Central Fighter Establishment), Wg Cdr H Bird-Wilson test flew a production F Mk 1 from the Chilbolton facility. In three flights on the 1st and 2nd he experienced three flame-outs (compressor stall). In discussions with Supermarine staff it became obvious that no-one at Supermarine or A&AEE had, at that time, tested the Swift at high angles of attack while pulling g at low indicated airspeeds. This was a problem that could only be overcome with a complete redesign of the air intakes.

On the 22nd October 1953 the Air Council announced that a squadron of Swifts (No.56 Squadron) was to be flying by the end of the calendar year. This heightened the need for C(A) release of the type so WK201 and

WK202 were sent to A&AEE Boscombe Down in January 1954 for clearance. Although one of their pilots had flown the Swift before (the very knowledgeable Sqn Ldr Clark having been killed on the 28th November 1953 in a collision with Valetta VW203 while flying Venom F Mk 1 WE258), by this stage it was quite late in the day for the ultimate customer of the type to actually test it, as production was already well under way. The AFDS collected three Swifts for further fighter evaluation trials on the 13th February 1954. The AFDS pilots soon found the type lacked longitudinal control in a high-speed dive; pulling back hard on the stick slightly raised the nose, but had little effect on changing the flightpath. By the 23rd February they reported that the type lacked elevator response even in level flight at maximum speed, so it was obvious that the Swift was not acceptable for operational service. The CFE put forward a list of critical improvements, the most important of these being an all-moving 'flying' tail. As related earlier, the Swift was tested in mock combat with the North American F-86 Sabre, and as some of the pilots with CFE at this time had combat experience from Korea, it soon highlighted the shortcoming in the Swift as far as being a fighter was concerned. Why neither Supermarine nor A&AEE had picked this up before can be explained by the fact that neither of these groups had had access to sufficiently advanced designs from other nations to allow them to have experience of what was needed in a modern fighter.

The F Mk 1 was cleared for service by the A&AEE in February 1954, but as a non-operational indoctrination fighter, and severe limitations in its flight envelope were imposed. Considering the loss of WJ965 and its pilot as recounted previously, A&AEE was extremely reluctant to issue any form of C(A) clearance, but had to because the allocation of the type to a squadron had been decreed by the Air Council. The restricted clearance issues for the F Mk 1 was never relaxed, as further trials showed that the type exhibited a range of undesirable aerodynamic characteristics, the worst of these being the pitch-up at high altitude and high indicated Mach numbers. The Air Ministry later requested the installation of four, rather than two 30mm Aden cannon, but production of the F Mk 1 was far too ad-

Swift F Mk 1 WK209 was the first to land at Waterbeach on the 20th February 1954 (©Air Ministry)

Swift F Mk 1 early production at South Marston alongside late model Spitfires (©Vickers)

vanced by this stage, so the initial order was curtailed and ceased after only eighteen had been built, with the entire Short and Harland order being cancelled.

F Mk 2

The first production F Mk 2 was WK214 and this airframe was fitted with four 30mm Aden cannon. Ammunition for the extra guns was housed in extensions to the inboard wing leading edges. Sadly this change in wing shape so altered the airflow that pitch-up occurred with even a very modest increase in the angle of attack above Mach 0.83. If a pilot pulled back too hard on the control column the nose would violently rear up and even with instant correction this could not prevent the aircraft from flipping over onto its back. The pitch-up was not violent enough to cause the pilot to black out, nor to overstress the airframe, but it was a tendancy that was not desirable in a fighter, as the height and time needed to correct it would render the aircraft highly vulnerable to attack during combat.

Very few images of in-service F Mk 2s exist, this one, although dark, shows WK242 operated by No 56 Squadron (©British Official)

After much testing the A&AEE project test pilot stated that regardless of the various modifications that had taken place, the Swift F Mk 2 remained "without exception, quite horrible to fly in one respect or another" and that it was "quite strongly stressed that such a policy (of modifications) can never make the Swift 2 a satisfactory or acceptable aircraft; any clearance issued to such a ma-

chine must inevitably be heavily restricted." In an effort to overcome the problem eight development modifications were made to the type, vortex generators were installed above and below the tailplanes, wing fences were installed and the leading edge of the outer wing was kinked (10% leading edge extension at the tip, starting at 60% semi-span) in the now-familiar 'saw-tooth' configuration. This only partially helped and a full cure was only found by once again moving the CofG much further forward (something that had also occurred progressively throughout the initial 'modifications'). Sadly this necessitated the fitment of ballast weights that totally ruined the high-altitude performance. It should be pointed out, though, that at this time most designers of high performance aircraft were having the same problems, and this even included Hawker with their new Hunter. The A&AEE pilots considered the modified F Mk 2 to be "most pleasant" to fly and that it was the first F Mk 2 that had "looked anything like a reasonable aircraft". It is therefore amazing to find that Supermarine

Many F Mk 2s ended their days as instructional airframes, this shows WK240, now marked as '7300M' and probably photographed at RAF Halton

intended these modifications only for the F Mk 3 and 4 versions, not as an improvement for the F Mk 2! In the end therefore only sixteen F Mk 2s were built and the type never received C(A) clearance for full service use, and only five of them were ever issued to a Squadron, these going to No.56 Squadron at Waterbeach. All of these saw service for less than a year before they were transferred to a Maintenance Unit and subsequently used as Instructional Airframes by the various Schools of Technical Training, with them being struck off charge in early 1956.

Swift F Mk 3 WK247 was the first of 25 delivered (©Ministry of Supply)

F Mk 3

The F Mk 3 was basically the modified F Mk 2 with reheat and the first production machine, WK247, flew for the first time in early 1953 and was shown to the public for the first time at Farnborough that year. The reheat engine had actually been trialled by Rolls-Royce using F Mk 1 WK195. The pitch-up tendencies of the F Mk 2 were still present, but only partially, and they could be controlled by the vortex generators on the tail surfaces. Both the F Mk 3 and later F Mk 4 were fitted with powered irreversible ailerons to counter the wing/aileron flutter problems of previous versions. By 1953 the Air Staff and the Ministry of Supply had decided that all non-reheat equipped Swifts would be considered non-operational, being used to allow the RAF to get experience in supersonic flight. Just 25 F Mk 3s were built and although perfectly flyable, most of these were delivered by road for use as instructional airframes and all of them were struck off charge in April 1956.

By this stage costs for the Swift had increased greatly from the estimated initial cost of £28,875 per unit to £65,000 and the Select Committee on (Parliamentary) Estimates at the time stated that "as the difficulties with the aircraft increased, so, it appeared, did the number on order". This statement on its own shows how distant the government was in relation to aviation projects at the time, and how little understanding there was with regard to the effects of Air Staff changes in the equipment and operational roles required of the Swift at such a late stage in its development.

F Mk 4

The first prototype for this version was a conversion of F Mk 1 WK198. It featured reheat, the saw-tooth wing and variable-incidence ('flying') tailplane. The type was also updated to production standard as per Air Ministry and Supermarine requirements and in this form it took to the air for the first time on the 2nd May 1953. On the 15th July, along with four F Mk 1s (WK197, WK202 and WJ965), Mike Lithgow flew WK198 as part of the Coronation Review at RAF Odiham. This was a great risk, as the Avon engines of the Swift

had proved problematical, with many complete compressor failures. The RAF wanted to have an example of their latest fighters in the flyplast to prove to everyone that no longer did they have to depend on overseas aid to obtain a modern swept-wing fighter, so the four Swifts and a Hunter were included at the end. Although the aircraft flew safely over Odiham, Mike Lithgow suffered complete compressor blade failure soon afterwards but thankfully made yet another power-off landing at Chilbolton. Numerous similar failures in the engines of production machines led to an investigation that found, much to Rolls-Royce's embarrassment, that one of the sub-contractors making the Avon Mk 105 for them had made a seemingly trivial change to the fir-tree root fixing for the compressor rotor blades to suits its manufacturing processes that had resulted in their failure, and all of these engines were those supplied to Supermarine for the Swift. Once these defective parts were replaced engine failures were far less common. The inclusion of the Swifts in the flypast had been at great expense to the overall test programme though, as the four machines were totally occupied with pilot familiarisation and formation flying practice for a six-week period in June and July prior to the event.

WK198 attended the Paris airshow on the 5th July 1953 and set a London-Paris record by covering the 212 miles in 19 minutes 5.6 seconds at an average speed of 669.3mph. After taking part in the 1953 SBAC show at Farnborough, WK198 was flown to Tripoli in North Africa to make an attempt at the World Absolute Air Speed Record. Mike Lithgow set a new record of 735.7mph on the 26th September and although two more runs of 737mph were achieved, during the third run the reheat failed so the speed could not be submitted for promulgation. Further attempts on the record were aborted when it was heard that the American Douglas F4D Skyray had achieved 753mph in one run. This type would later go on to set a new record of 752.94mph on the 3rd October. WK198 remained on Ministry of Supply charge as a manufacturer's test airframe until 1957, when it was sent to No.23 MU RAF Aldergrove. After just a year with No.10 School of Technical Training, it was struck off charge and sold as scrap to Unimetals. The remains of the fuselage without

Brand new F Mk 3s awaiting collection at South Marston (©Ministry of Supply)

Although the F Mk 4 was never used operationally there are a good few shots of this machine, WK273, seen here on display at Farnborough with eight 3in rocket projectiles under the port wing and (not visible) a 500lb bomb under the starboard

wings were found at the Unimetals' yard at Failsworth, Manchester and thankfully saved from destruction in 1981. Today the fuselage resides with the North East Aircraft Museum at Sunderland Airport.

The constant modifications had led the Swift to become progressively heavier and as a result by the time the F Mk 3 and 4 came along it was no longer able to fulfil a role as a fighter. Reheat had to be used for take-off, climb and combat and this resulted in an endurance of just 25 minutes and a combat radius of barely 50 miles, Still, many who flew or tested the F Mk 4 considered it to be on the verge of being the best day fighter in production at that time, but in the end only eight F Mk 4s were built (WK272 to WK279). Many state that all of these were retained by Supermarine and converted into FR Mk 5s, as was the case for the remaining thirty-one F Mk 4s then on order, but a detailed check of the history of each serial number proves this to be incorrect. WK272 was used by the A&AEE and scrapped in 1955, WK273 was used by the manufacturer and ended up on a fire dump in 1959, WK274, 276, 277 and 278 were all converted to FR Mk 5s, while WK275 was used for trials (and still exists today) and WK279 was never issued to a unit, ending up as an Instruction Airframe before being SOC in October 1957.

The whole Swift programme was cancelled in February 1954, after 176 airframes had been completed. Many have said that the problems experienced throughout Swift development and service use up to this date had been greatly exaggerated to justify cancelling the project at this stage. The truth is probably that it was an excuse, but that this was brought about by the general decrease in world tension at this time and the fact that production of both Swift and Hunter would have thus been excessive, so one of them had to go.

FR Mk 5

The Swift had proved unsuitable in its intended interceptor role, so it was decided to convert the type for low-altitude, high-speed

tactical reconnaissance. The FR Mk 5 (Type 549) was basically an F Mk 4 with a lengthened nose to house three F.95 cameras, one of which was mounted in the extreme nose, the other two on either side for oblique photography. This camera installation had first been tested in modified F Mk 1 WK200 during 1953. The type was armed with two 30mm Aden cannon and had a 200 Imp. Gal. ventral tank fitted as standard. The first FR Mk 5, XD903, made its first flight on the 27th May 1955 and this was followed by the next two production machines, XD904 & XD905, both of which featured a clear-view canopy. At last a British design had the framless 'blown' canopy so admired previously on the F-86 Sabre, but although the production had been mastered in the UK, the materials used all came from America. Being a development of the F Mk 4, the FR Mk 5 also featured the (1ft) taller vertical fin and wing racks for 2,000lb of bombs or rockets. With the F Mk 4 never having reached squadron service, the FR Mk 5 was the first production machine to reach RAF squadron service that was fitted with reheat. Although this gave the type the edge slightly over the Hunter F Mk 6, the fuel consumption was so huge that it was rarely

used as it could eat up the excellent 998 Gallon fuel load at low-level in an alarmingly short length of time!

In all 94 FR Mk 5s were constructed, 35 of these being converted from F Mk 4s; four converted from complete F Mk 4s: WK274, 276, 277 & 278), while the remainder were the initial F Mk 4 contract (WK280, 281 and WK287 to WK315.

PR Mk 6

This version was intended as an unarmed photo-reconnaissance development requiring the minimum change from the basic F Mk 4 and was designated the Type 550. The design featured the extended camera nose of the FR Mk 5 and it was intended to replace the Meteor PR Mk 10. Many sources state that this design utilised the extended span wing of the F Mk 7, but research by Phil Spenser has disproved this claim and the PR Mk 6 (Type 550) was intended to retain the shorter span of the F Mk 4. The type would have mounted two F.52 cameras one each side of the air intakes (between frames 17 & 18) and a further F.49 unit on a hinged panel by Frame 16. The option to fit F.96 cameras in lieu of the F.52 was also included. The type would not

A unique shot showing Swift F Mk 4 WK275 up on ramps for noise trials at Hatfield. This aircraft still exists and is in restoration with Jet Art Aviation

Swift F Mk 1 WK200 was the aerodynamic prototype for the FR Mk 5 series (©Ministry of Supply)

carry the usual 200 Gallon drop tank, as this partially obscured the cameras, so instead it would have had 100 Gallon drops tanks on pylons under each wing and additional internal tanks in the redundant space left by the removal of the guns and ammunition. Development of this type was slow, and various changes led ultimately to partial abandonment of the 'minimum change' concept. The single prototype, XD143, was cancelled in early 1955, when it was nearing completion (it was scheduled to fly in March) and the contract for it was officially cancelled on the 25th April. The partial airframe was delivered in a dismantled state to RAF Halton and allocated Instruction Airframes No.7289M. The number was never applied and it appears that the airframe was never unpacked or used. Its derelict remains were photographed at Halton ready for scrapping on the 6th September 1956 and it is presumed it was actually scrapped soon afterwards.

A nice shot of an FR Mk 5 that we believe is WK281, seen at an airshow but nowadays owned by the RAF Museum and on loan to Tangmere

F Mk 7

This mark was based on a design study from August 1952 that looked at arming the type with a combination of four Blue Sky air-to-air missiles and four Aden cannon. The Blue Sky missile came about as the result of an Operational Requirement issued in May 1949. It

was intended to attack perceived formations of Russian bombers but was only ever seen as an interim type for 'limited application' in daylight. The missile was a beam rider, and the GGS (Gyroscopic Gunsight) Mk 9 and Radar Ranging Mk 2 equipment in the Swift had to be held on the target throughout, so the missile could ride the beam of the radar which was 'illuminating' the target. The radar to generate the guidance beam resulted in the lengthening of the nose and the type also had

an increase of 3ft in the wing span to accommodate the four associated pylons. A larger powerplant with optimised nozzle was also required and for this the Rolls-Royce Avon 716 was selected. The type also featured the 'flying' slab tailplane with datum-trimming first tested by F Mk 4 WK275. To test the proposals F Mk 4 WK279 was used as an aerodynamic test-best. Modified to represent the proposed F Mk 7, it was fitted with the detachable launchers for the Blue Sky missiles

A well-known shot of Swift FR Mk 5 with No 2 Squadron at Geilenkirchen, Germany (©Air Ministry/MOD)

A nice shot of Swift FR Mk 5 WK277. This aircraft still exists and is on display at Newark

and three of these were successfully launched in October 1955.

The first production F Mk 7, XF774, flew on the 29th March 1956, with the second, XF780, following in June. Both these first two machines can be considered as pre-production prototypes for the series and they were followed by the first production machine in August. All three machines plus WK279 went to A&AEE Boscombe Down in September to undertake handling trials. XF774 and XF780 were later sent to RAF Valley for guided weapons trials, as the trials at Boscombe Down had only been to determine the maximum permitted speed with pylons and missiles fitted. At Valley XF780 was fitted with cameras in the nose and flew alongside XF774 to record firing of the missiles. The planned production run of 75 aircraft was reduced to 12 (XF113-124) and these were developed from the F Mk 4 at a total cost of just £92,000! XF774 was finally used by RAE as a structural test airframes and XF780 was sold for scrap in 1958

One former Supermarine staff member stated that the F Mk 7 was "the finest and most effective aircraft/weapons combination available to the RAF at that time". Sadly it was to be a case of too little too late, as by this time neither the government nor the RAF had any wish to develop or use the Swift, and it was consigned, along with the Blue Sky (Fireflash) missile, to the scrapheap.

In Service

F Mk 1

The F Mk 1 entered service with No.56 Squadron at RAF Waterbeach on the 13th February 1954. As recounted earlier the type was only cleared as a non-operational fighter for indoctrination. The restrictions imposed meant that the squadron could not climb

above 25,000ft, exceed 550knots to 5,000ft and Mach 0.91 above this, nor could they spin the aircraft, strict limits were imposed on both positive and negative g manoeuvres and it was strictly forbidden to use the type in a ground-attack role. Initially the type suffered a poor serviceability rate, but this is nothing unusual in a jet of that era, and was certainly no worse than was to be the

case with early designs like the Javelin (See Gloster Javelin - The RAF's First Delta Wing Fighter by this author, ISBN: 1-905414-02-1) and Lightning.

The squadron lost, in quick succession, two aircraft, thankfully without loss of life. The first was WK209, when the CO decided to investigate the low-speed handling of the type. While undertaking a stall in the

Official image of FR Mk 5 WK295 from No.79 Squadron flying past the Hermannsdenkmal at Lippe, West Germany (©British Official)

approach configuration, the aircraft yawed to starboard and entered a spin to port that the pilot could not recover from. Having attempted just about every spin-recovery technique, he was forced to eject just below 10,000ft. The second was a pilot who failed to activate the powered ailerons correctly. This second event led to the fleet being grounded on a temporary basis, while this situation was investigated.

No.56 was the only squadron to operate the Swift in the fighter role, and after numerous problems and incidents it was obviously unsuitable for service use, so it was withdrawn in March 1955 and the squadron re-equipped with the Hunter in May.

F Mk 2

It was also to be No.56 Squadron at Waterbeach that was the first and only squadron to receive the F Mk 2, when its first examples arrived on the 30th August 1954. These machines had the four 30mm Aden cannon installed, but the type was forbidden to carry ammunition and the nose was filled with ballast in an attempt to correct the trim problems mentioned previously. As with the F Mk 1, the Mk 2 also proved to be unsuitable for service use as a fighter and was withdrawn along with the F Mk 1s in March 1955.

Five withdrawn airframes (Only WK216 and WK217 are listed, although WK215, WK221 and WK239 are the other three) were later used along with F Mk 1 WK199 in Operation Buffalo at Marilinga in Australia to test the effects of exposure to a nuclear burst. Although only two of these were written off during the trials, all of them were broken up on site and buried.

Lovely shot as FR Mk 5 XD907 goes over the top of a loop (©Air Minstry)

F Mk 3

The F Mk 3 was never used operationally. 23 airframes were delivered to the RAF and all of them were sent via road and only used as instructional airframes at various training bases.

F Mk 4

Most sources state that no F Mk 4s were used operationally and that is technically correct, because those airframes built as F Mk 4s that were allocated to units, only did so once they had been converted to

FR Mk 5s. They were WK274 and WK277, which were operated by No.2 Squadron and WK276, used by No.79 Squadron.

FR Mk 5

The first FR Mk 5s began to re-equip No.2 (Army Co-operation) Squadron, 2nd TAF (Tactical Air Force) initially at RAF Geilenkirchen, West Germany on the 23rd February 1956. The squadron was, at this time, commanded by Sqn Ldr R S 'Bunny' Mortley, but full operational readiness was not easy to achieve due to the combination of bad weather and poor serviceability. So bad was the situation that Supermarine was forced to send a team out to the squadron to try to get over the problems. Flight hours steadily increased as serviceability improved and during October 1957 the squadron moved to Jever. Command of the squadron was handed over to Sqn Ldr C Wade in April 1958 and he was succeeded by Sqn Ldr 'Mac' MacDonald in September 1960. The squadron converted to the Hunter FR Mk 10 in March 1961, thus effectively ending the Swift's operational career.

The second squadron to operate the FR Mk 5 was No.79 Squadron, 2nd TAF, which was also based in West Germany. This squadron received its first example on the 14th June 1956, when it was based at Wunstorf and commanded by Sqn Ldr N K 'Mac' McCallum. The squadron moved to Gütersloh in August that year and in February 1957 the CO was succeeded by Sqn Ldr Hugh Harrison. In April that year the squadron took part in Exercise Guest in which it undertook numerous sorties against early warning and fire control radar systems. During the annual NATO reconnaissance competition Royal Flush II at

Air-to-air photo sortie with FR Mk 5 XD907 (©Air Ministry)

Swift FR Mk 5 WK290 previously operated by No.2 Squadron and probably seen here awaiting its fate on the fire dump

F Mk 7

Eleven of the twelve F Mk 7s built were allocated to No.1 Guided Weapons Development Squadron at RAF Valley. This unit was formed in March 1957 under the command of Wg Cdr J O 'Joe' Daley and undertook test firing of the Fairey Blue Sky (later Fireflash) air-to-air beam-riding missile over Cardigan Bay. Although no live warheads were ever fired in the UK, over 160 firings were completed, although not all of these were with the Swift. Once the trials were concluded, the airframes were sent to No.23 MU, RAF Aldergrove where most were eventually scrapped. The exception to this was XF113, which eventually wound up with the Empire Test Pilots' School at RAF Farnborough, where it remained until 1962. Today the nose section of this aircraft is part of the Boscombe Down Aviation Collection at Old Sarum.

Laarbruch in May 1957, FR Mk 5s of Nos.79 and 2 Squadrons came first and second respectively ahead of a mixed bag of NATO RF-84F Thunderjets, a feat they would repeat in 1959 during Royal Flush IV. In September the squadron was involved in Exercise Brown Jug and in March 1958 it was able to operate two of its Swifts from the packed snow of Norway during Exercise Northern Lights. The squadron took top honours and the Sassoon Trophy during March 1959 which unlike the Royal Flush exercises, was a trophy specific to the RAF Tactical Reconnaissance squadrons in Germany. Of the thirty-three FR Mk 5s operated by No.79 Squadron during

from Jever on the 13th April 1961. Those in the UK were stored at No.60 MU, Church Fenton or No.23 MU, Aldergrove. Nearly all of these were allocated Instructional Airframe numbers and assigned to various training and ATC (Air Training Corps) units for instructional use. Some were not allocated and after a period in store were scrapped, but two were preserved with WK277 going to the Newark Air Museum and WK281 being allocated to the RAF Museum's collection. The latter spent a number of years on display at Hendon before being put on long-term loan to the Tangmere Military Aviation Museum, where it resides today.

The only F Mk 7 not to be operated by No.1 GWDS was XF114, which went to C Squadron at A&AEE Boscombe Down. Initially it was used for pilot familiarisation work, but in November 1960 it undertook a Ministry contract to test various runway surfaces (asphalt, concrete and 'natural slush'). These trials continued at Filton and Wisley and between the 25th May and 6th June 1962 the aircraft did a number of landings at Heathrow. These were to assess landings on a wet runway at speeds in excess of 180mph and were in relation to new high-speed designs such as the BAC TSR.2. By this stage the all-black painted aircraft was operated by the College of Technology at Cranfield, Bedfordshire and it remained with this institution until being moved to the College of Technology at Kelsterton. Here it languished until the late 1980s, when it was sold to Jet Heritage Ltd at Hurn Airport. The intention was to restore the aircraft, but it remained a low priority and when Jet Heritage Ltd went into liquidation in 1998 the airframe moved into store at RAF Scampton. It was eventually put up for sale and acquired by the Southampton Hall of Aviation (later renamed Solent Sky) and as we write it is stored by them awaiting restoration. Sadly

A Fireflash missile is loaded aboard a Swift F Mk 7 during trials (©British Official/MOD)

their four years of service, seven were lost to accidents. Most of these were due to engine failures, but one was fatal and was caused by the canopy detaching after take-off. On the 1st January 1961 No.79 was renumbered as No.4 Squadron and began to convert to the Hawker Hunter. A dwindling number of Swifts remained with the squadron during this conversion, but all had departed within a few months.

With the withdrawal of the type, some of those damaged during the final months of service were simply written off, as it was not worth repairing them. Some of these were scrapped in Germany but most came back to the UK. The last to leave was WK289

A Swift F Mk 7 fires a Fireflash missile during trials (©British Official/MOD)

Specifications

Designation: Type 525/535
First Flight: 27/03/50 (as 525), 23/08/50 (as 535)
Span: 31ft 8 1/2in
Length: 41ft 4in
Engine: One Rolls-Royce Nene RN.2 with 5,100lb thrust
Take-off Weight: 14,390lb
Max speed: 656mph
Armament: Four 20mm cannon (not fitted)
Production: 1 (VV119)

Day Interceptor Fighter & Ground Attack

Designation: F Mk 1
First Flight: 01/08/51 (WJ960), 18/07/52 (WJ965), 25/08/52 (F Mk 1 production)
Span: 32ft 4in   Length: 41ft 5 1/2in
Height: 12ft 6in
Engine: One Rolls-Royce Avon (RA.7) 10501 straight-flow turbojet with 7,500lb thrust
Take-off Weight: 15,800lb
Max speed: 689mph (sea level), 618mph (30,000ft)
Rate of Climb @ Sea Level: 12,300ft/min
Operational Ceiling: 45,400ft
Range: 730 miles
Armament: Two 30mm Aden cannon with 200 rounds per gun
Ejection Seat: Martin-Baker Mk 2G
Production: 20 +2 prototypes

Designation: F Mk 2
First Flight: 31/05/54 (WK214)
Span: 32ft 4in   Length: 41ft 5 1/2in
Height: 12ft 6in
Engine: One Rolls-Royce Avon (RA.7) 10501 axial-flow turbojet with 7,500lb thrust
Take-off Weight: 19,764lb
Max speed: 709mph
Rate of Climb @ Sea Level: 14,540ft/min
Operational Ceiling: 39,000ft
Range: 493 miles
Armament: Two 30mm Aden cannon (with 185 rounds per gun (aft tank))or
Four 30mm Aden cannon (with 135 rounds (front tank) and 165 (aft tank) per gun)
Ejection Seat: Martin-Baker Mk 2G
Production: 16

Designation: F Mk 3
Span: 32ft 4in
Length (wheels on ground): 41ft 5 1/2in
Height (top of fin, wheels on ground): 12ft 3in (approx.)
Engine: One Rolls-Royce Avon 10801 axial-flow turbojet with 7,500lb thrust
Take-off Weight: 19,135lb
Armament: Four 30mm Aden cannon with 150 rounds per gun
Ejection Seat: Martin-Baker Mk 2G
Radio Equipment: A.R.I.5490 (wireless), A.R.I.5131, 5849 & 5857 (radar)
Production: 25

Designation: F Mk 4
Span: 32ft 4in
Length (wheels on ground): 41ft 6in
Height (top of fin, wheels on ground): 12ft 3in
Engine: One Rolls-Royce Avon 114 straight-flow turbojet with 7,500lb thrust
Weight: 13,136 (Tare), 19,764lb (Loaded)
Max speed: 709mph @ Sea Level
Rate of Climb @ Sea Level:
Service Ceiling: 39,000ft (without reheat)
Range: 493 Miles
Armament: Two or four 30mm Aden cannon with 150 rounds per gun in four-gun configuration or 200 rounds per gun in two-gun (outboard) configuration. Provision to carry 1,000lb bomb on a pylon under each wing or sixteen rocket projectiles
Ejection Seat: Martin-Baker Mk 2G
Radio Equipment: A.R.I.5490 (wireless) and A.R.I.5131, 5849 & 5857 (radar)
Production: 8

Low-level Tactical Reconnaissance

Designation: FR Mk 5
Span: 32ft 4in
Length: 42ft 3in
Height: 13.2ft
Engine: One Rolls-Royce Avon 114 co-axial with 7,175lb [9,450lb with reheat] thrust
Take-off Weight: 21,250lb
Max speed: 691mph (clean), 674mph (with ventral tank)
Rate of Climb @ Sea Level: 14,660ft/min
Operational Ceiling: 45,800ft
Range: 630 miles
Armament: Two 30mm Aden cannon & eight 3in unguided rocket projectiles. Also carried two strip-aperture F.95 oblique cameras
Production: 90

Photo Reconnaissance

Designation: PR Mk 6
First Flight: N/A
Armament: None
Cameras: Two F.52 cameras one each side of the air intakes (between frames 17 & 18) and a further F.49 unit on a hinged panel by Frame 16. Option to fit F.96 cameras in lieu of the F.52 was also available.
Production: 1 (Prototype only)

Missile-armed Interceptor

Designation: F Mk 7
Span (wheels on ground): 36ft 1in
Length (wheels on ground): 44ft 1/2in
Height (top of fin, wheels on ground): 13ft 2in, (maximum height, oleos fully extended) 14ft 1 1/2in
Engine: One Rolls-Royce Avon 716 straight-flow turbojet with 7,550lb [9,950lb with reheat] thrust
Weight: 13,735lb (Tare), 21,400lb (Loaded)
Max speed: 691mph (clean), 668mph (with two missiles)
Operational Ceiling: 41,600ft
Range: 864 miles
Armament: Two 30mm Aden cannon and two or four Fairey Fireflash Beam-riding Air-to-Air missiles
Ejection Seat: Martin-Baker Mk 3G
Radio Equipment: A.R.I.18064 [VHF wireless], A.R.I.5849 (Rebecca Mk 7) or A.R.I.23013 (Rebecca Mk 8) [radar]
Production: 14

Note: We have refrained from making conversions from Imperial to Metric as far as dimensions go, as these would always be approximations at best and as the type was built to the Imperial standard, we have just included these dimensions in the above specifications

Nice official shot of an F Mk 7, probably XF774, operated by the GWDS for Fireflash trials (©MOD)

Swift F Mk 7 XF118 of No.1 GWDS seen on display at an airshow with dummy Fireflash missiles attached

Swift F Mk 7 XF114 being operated by the RAE for runway surface trials at Heathrow, seen alongside a BEA Vanguard

this restoration will only be to static condition, so the chance of a Swift taking to the air once again is now finally over.

Type 545

No account of the Swift would be complete without mention of this machine. It was based on the proposal for a supersonic Swift that had followed after the relative success of the Type 510. It was accepted by the Air Ministry in March 1951 and in February 1952 an order for two prototypes was placed against Specification F.105D2. The airframe that emerged had the compound sweep of the later Swifts with 50 degrees of sweep on the inner and 30 degrees on the outer panels. The fuselage featured area-rule and the air intakes were moved forward to the nose, well ahead of the wings. This intake was split with a bullet-shaped central body thus avoiding the need for a bypass bleed, while the lower fuselage at the junction with the wings was flattened and featured large fillets to avoid the low-speed drag encountered with the Swift.

The first prototype, XA181, was to be fitted with the Rolls-Royce RA.14 engine, while the second, XA186, was to have the RA.35R or RB.106. These engines gave an estimated top speed of Mach 1.3 of 1.68 respectively. XA181 was nearing completion when the whole project was cancelled, while XA186 was never completed. XA181 did survive for

a time as part of the College of Aeronautics collection at Cranfield, but was ultimately broken up for scrap in the 1970s. The only piece known to survive is the canopy, which is held by the Midland Air Museum.

In Retrospect

Many claim the Swift was a failure, and in parts this is true. Certainly in its intended role as an interceptor it was lacking, but this was mainly due to the ever-changing requirements of the Air Staff at the time, and the explosion of knowledge in the transonic and supersonic regimes that were all part and parcel of the post-war period. The demand for increased armament, coupled with an already unstable airframe led to a totally unsuitable aircraft. This was not the fault of the Swift design, more of the fact that both the Air Staff and Supermarine tried to meet the demands of the period without redesigning the Swift to fully incorporate current aerodynamic knowledge.

The Swift did a huge amount of pioneering work, and the rigours of the low-level operations undertaken by the type allowed both the RAE and Supermarine to develop and understand the stresses that an airframe withstood during repeated low-level, high-g manoeuvres. The type was never beaten in low-level operations, even by more advanced

American designs that utilised much of the aerodynamic data recovered from Nazi Germany at the end of WWII. The F Mk 7 was the first to deploy a guided weapon in the shape of the Fireflash and was the first operational British aircraft to have reheat, all of which helped in the subsequent development of types such as the English Electric Lightning.

It is sad to note that when the Select Committee on (Parliamentary) Estimates commented with regard to the escalating cost of the type, the entire intended production run of 492 aircraft then on order would have cost around £27 million, a figure that even by the late 1970s would have only have bought you a couple of new frontline fighters!

Conversion Chart
Imperial

1 nautical mile (nm) = 1.136 statute miles	
1 mile per hour (mph) = 0.88 knots	
1 Imperial Gallon - 7.2lb	
Imperial to Metric	
1 foot (ft) = 0.3048 metres (m)	
1 nautical mile (nm) = 1.828 kilometres (km)	
1 square foot = 0.0929 square metres	
1ft per minutes = 0.005m/sec	
1 mile per hour (mph) = 1.61 kilometre per hour (km/h)	
1 pound (lb) = 0.454 kilograms (kg)	
1 Gallon = 4.546 litres	

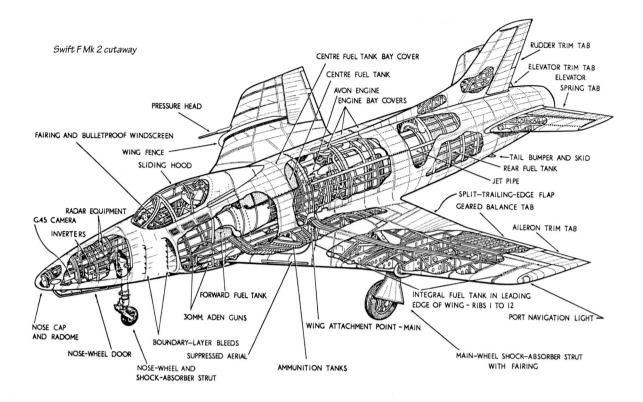

Swift F Mk 2 cutaway

RUDDER TRIM TAB
ELEVATOR TRIM TAB
ELEVATOR
SPRING TAB
CENTRE FUEL TANK BAY COVER
CENTRE FUEL TANK
AVON ENGINE
ENGINE BAY COVERS
PRESSURE HEAD
FAIRING AND BULLETPROOF WINDSCREEN
WING FENCE
SLIDING HOOD
TAIL BUMPER AND SKID
REAR FUEL TANK
JET PIPE
SPLIT-TRAILING-EDGE FLAP
GEARED BALANCE TAB
AILERON TRIM TAB
RADAR EQUIPMENT
G.45 CAMERA
INVERTERS
FORWARD FUEL TANK
30MM ADEN GUNS
INTEGRAL FUEL TANK IN LEADING
EDGE OF WING - RIBS 1 TO 12
PORT NAVIGATION LIGHT
NOSE CAP
AND RADOME
WING ATTACHMENT POINT - MAIN
NOSE-WHEEL DOOR
BOUNDARY-LAYER BLEEDS
SUPPRESSED AERIAL
MAIN-WHEEL SHOCK-ABSORBER STRUT
WITH FAIRING
NOSE-WHEEL AND
SHOCK-ABSORBER STRUT
AMMUNITION TANKS

Section 1

Technical Description

What follows is an extensive selection of images and diagrams that will help you understand the physical nature of the Swift series. Note that we have refrained from covering the various prototypes (Type 510 & 525/535) or projected (Type 545) airframes in this section, keeping it purely focussed on just the Swift in pre-production (Type 541) and production (Mks 1 to 7) forms.

© All images copyright the author
unless otherwise noted

Swift F Mk 1 cutaway

NOTE:- CENTRE FUEL TANK OMITTED FROM
THE TANK BAY FOR CLARITY

1	NOSE CAP AND RADOME	13	JET PIPE	25	LEADING-EDGE WING TANK
2	RADAR	14	FUSELAGE REAR TANK	26	WING MAIN ATTACHMENT TO FUSELAGE
3	RUDDER BAR	15	PRESSURE HEAD	27	AMMUNITION BAY
4	CONTROL COLUMN	16	RUDDER TRIM TAB	28	30 MM. ADEN GUN
5	B.P. WINDSCREEN AND FAIRING	17	REAR FAIRING CONE	29	DROP TANK
6	EJECTOR SEAT	18	ELEVATOR SPRING TAB	30	AIR-INTAKE
7	SLIDING HOOD	19	TAIL BUMPER AND SKID	31	BOUNDARY- LAYER BLEED
8	FUSELAGE FORWARD TANK	20	SPLIT-TRAILING-EDGE FLAP	32	NOSE WHEEL SHOCK - ABSORBER STRUT
9	CENTRE TANK BAY COVER	21	AILERON SPRING TAB	33	NOSE-WHEEL DOOR
10	WIRELESS (STB'D) RADAR (PORT)	22	AILERON TRIM TAB	34	G.45 CAMERA
11	ENGINE BAY COVERS	23	NAVIGATION LIGHT		
12	AVON ENGINE	24	SHOCK-ABSORBER STRUT WITH FAIRING		

1.1 Cockpit Interior

Swift F Mks 1 and 2 – Controls and equipment in cockpit
(©Crown Copyright)

Key
1. Jettisonable tank jettison control
   Pull up to jettison
2. Crowbar
3. IFF 'D' switch
   On – Forward
   Off – Alt
4. Flaps lowering push button
5. Alighting gear lowering push button
6. Cockpit ventilator
7. Main accumulator air pressure gauges
   (Indicate air pressure available for
   lowering alighting gear and flaps)
8. Aileron trim control switch
   (manual flying only)
   Press to port to lower port main plane
   Press to starboard to raise port main plane
9. Elevator trim hand wheel
   Rotate sharply to break soft locking wire
   Forward – Nose down
   Alt – Nose up
10. Hood jettison handle
    Pull aft to release
11. Alighting gear up push button pre-loading
    release ring
    Rotate clockwise, then push to retract alighting
    gear when brakes have failed
12. Fire warning and push button (jet pipe)
13. Fire warning lamp and push button
    (engine bay)
14. GGS manual retraction control
    Push forward to retract
15. E2 compass
16. E2 compass correction card
17. Bombs large R.Bs "defuse then jettison"
    push button
18. Oxygen emergency flow control
    Press inboard or outboard: also used

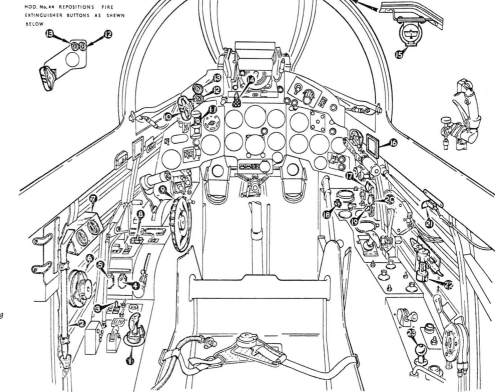

to test mask
19. Cockpit emergency lighting switch
20. "Jettison small R.B." push button
21. Hood seal emergency release

Push forward to release seal pressure
22. Access key (pre Mod.309)
Started access panels, ammunition boxes, gun
bay doors, first aid equipment (Post Mod.309,

on aft face of frame 13, in aircraft destructor
stowage on starboard side of fuselage)
23. Emergency oxygen supply control
Automatic supply release upon ejection

Swift F Mks 1 and 2 – Flying controls and instruments
(©Crown Copyright)

Key
1. Elevator power selector
   On – Forward
   Off – Alt
2. Rudder trim control switch
   Press outboard – Trim to port
   Press inboard – Trim to starboard
3. Elevator trim indicator
4. Ailerons and rudder trim indicator
5. Aileron power selector
   On – Up
   Off – Down
6. Flaps/air brakes control switch
   Up – Forward
   Off – Centre
   Airbrakes out (flaps down) – Alt
   Operate after pre-setting movement limit
   with 8
7. Wheel brakes triple-reading pressure gauge
8. Flaps down position limit switch
   Take-off and air brakes – Up
   Landing – Down
9. Flaps position indicator
10. Alighting gear selector push-buttons
    Up – Push upper button
    Down – Push lower button
11. Pressure heat heating switch
    On – Up
    Off – Down
12. MACH meter
13. Alighting gear position indicator
    Three green lights – All units locked down
    Three red lights – All units unlocked
    Red (centre only) – All units locked up, throttle
    back
14. Accelerometer
15. Instrument flying panel
16. Aileron power indicator
17. Rudder pedals
18. Cockpit altimeter

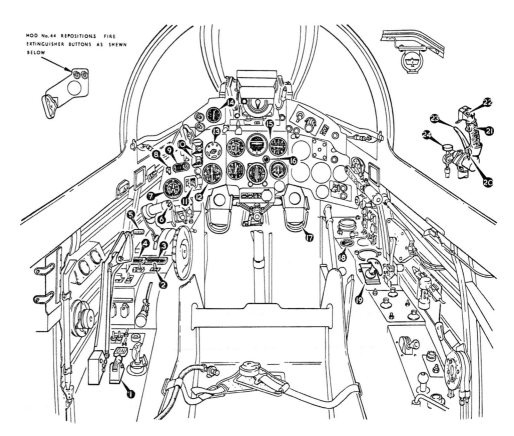

19. Rudder bar adjustment control
    Pull up to release catch
20. Wheel-brakes lever parking lock
21. Control column hand grip
22. Elevator trim control switch
    Push forward – Trim nose down

Push aft – Trim nose up
23. Wheel brakes control lever
24. Aileron trim control (use with power ON)
    Raise left wing – Rotate clockwise
    Raise right wing – Rotate anti-clockwise

Swift F Mk 3 – Flying controls and instruments (©Crown Copyright)

Key

1. Elevator power selector
   On – Forward; Off – Alt
2. Aileron trim control switch
   (manual flying only)
   Press to port – To lower port main plane
   Press to starboard – To raise port main plane
3. Rudder trim control switch
   Press to port – To turn nose to port
   Press to starboard – To turn nose to starboard
4. Ailerons and rudder trim indicator
5. Elevator trim indicator
6. Aileron power selector
   On – Up; Off – Down
7. Air brakes (flaps) control switch
   use item 9 to pre-set 'down' limit
   In – Press forward end
   Out – Press aft end
8. Wheel brakes triple-reading pressure gauge
9. Flaps 'down' position limit switch
   Take-off and air brakes – Up
   Landing – Down
10. Flaps position indicator
11. Alighting gear selector push buttons
    Up – Push upper button
    Down – Push lower button
12. Accelerometer
13. Alighting gear position indicator
    Three green lights – All units locked down
    Three red lights – All units unlocked
    Red (centre only) – All units locked up,
    throttle back
14. Instrument flying panel
15. Pressure heat heating switch
    On – Up; Off – Down
16. MACH meter
17. Aileron power indicator lamp
    Green – Power unit engaged
18. Elevator power indicator lamp
    Green – Power unit engaged
19. Power controls indicator lamp

Red (flashing) – Power controls unsafe
20. Aileron trim control (use with power ON)
    Raise left wing – Rotate clockwise
    Raise right wing – Rotate anti-clockwise
21. Wheel-brakes control lever

22. Elevator trim control switch
    Push forward – Trim nose down
    Push aft – Trim nose up
23. Control column hand grip
24. Wheel-brakes lever parking lock

25. Rudder pedals
26. Cockpit altimeter
27. Rudder bar adjustment control
    Pull up to release catch

Swift F Mk 3 – Engine controls and equipment (©Crown Copyright)

Key

1. High pressure fuel cock lever
   (press trigger before pushing down)
   On – Up; Off – Down
2. Engine re-light switch
   Press down to re-light
3. Reheat low-pressure fuel cock lever
   On – Forward; Off – Aft
4. Engine low-pressure fuel cock lever
   On – Forward; Off – Aft
5. Engine and air intakes ant-icing control
   Open – Forward; Closed – Aft
6. Throttle control lever
   Open – Forward; Closed – Aft
7. Fuel auto override switch
   Use when jettisonable tank is fitted
   Take-off – Up; Normal – Down
8. Fuel pump isolation switch
   Not in use
9. Fuel pump isolation indicator
   Not in use
10. Jet pipe nozzle position indicator
    White – Nozzle not fully open with reheat on
    Nozzle not fully open with reheat off
    Black – Nozzle position correct
11. Hot gas warning lamp
    Amber – Hot gas entering zone 3
12. Air extraction indicator
    White – Valve not fully open with
    alighting gear down
    Valve fully closed with alighting gear up
    Black – Valve position correct
13. Starter master switch
    On – Up; Off – Down
14. Ignition switch
    On – Up; Off – Down
15. Fuel master switch
    On – Up; Off – Down
16. Starter push button
17. Engine surge indicator
18. Forward generator failure warning indicator
    Black – Charging
    White – Not charging
19. After generator failure warning indicator
    Black – Charging; White – Not charging

20. Fuel flow failure warning indicators
    Black – Normal
    White – Jettisonable tank supplying
    (or fuel supply failure if jettisonable tank
    not fitted or empty)
21. Fuel pressure warning indicator
    Black – Normal; White – Low
22. Fuel contents gauge

23. Fuel balancing indicator
    White – Nose heavy; Black – Normal
24. Fuel balancing indicator
    White – Tail heavy; Black – Normal
25. Fuel balancing re-trim switch
    Retrim – Nose heavy
    Auto
    Retrim – Tail heavy

26. Jettisonable tank empty indicator
    White – Tank empty
27. Oil pressure indicator
28. Jet pipe temperature gauge
29. Engine speed indicator

This is an overall shot of the instrument panel in F Mk 4 WK275 when it was opened for the first time in about 50 years in 2012! (©Jet Art Aviation Ltd)

This is the port side upper element of the instrument panel in F Mk 4 WK275 (©Jet Art Aviation Ltd)

This is the starboard side upper element of the instrument panel in F Mk 4 WK275 (©Jet Art Aviation Ltd)

This is an overall view of the what is left of the instrument panel in the FR Mk 5 (WK281) owned by the RAF Museum

This is the upper port side element of the instrument panel in FR Mk 5 WK281

An overall view of the upper section of the instrument panel in the F Mk 7 cockpit section displayed by the Boscombe Down Aviation Collection [BDAC]

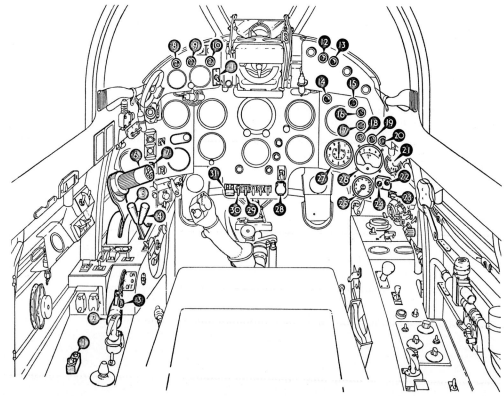

Swift F Mk 7 – Engine controls and equipment (©Crown Copyright)

Key

1. Ignition circuit breaker
2. High pressure fuel cock lever
(press trigger before pushing down)
    On – Up; Off – Down
3. Engine re-light switch
    Press down to re-light
4. Reheat low-pressure fuel cock lever
    On – Forward; Off – Aft
5. Engine low-pressure fuel cock lever
    On – Forward; Off – Aft
6. Throttle control lever
    Open – Forward; Closed – Aft
7. Top temperature override control switch
    Override – Up; Normal – Down
8. Jet pipe nozzle position indicator
White – Nozzle not fully open with reheat on
    Nozzle not fully open with reheat off
    Black – Nozzle position correct
9. Hot gas warning lamp
    Amber – Hot gas entering zone 3
10. Air extraction indicator
    White – Valve not fully open with
    alighting gear down
Valve fully closed with alighting gear up
    Black – Valve position correct
11. Reheat shut-off switch
    Normal – Up; Off – Down
12. Forward generator failure warning indicator
    Black – Charging; White – Not charging
13. After generator failure warning indicator
    Black – Charging; White – Not charging
14. Port gun bay (fuselage side) tank indicator
    Black – Normal; White – Empty
15. Fuel pressure warning indicator
    Black – Normal; White – Low
16–20. Fuel flow failure warning indicators
    Black – Normal; White – Fuel failure
Note – The item numbers relate to forward,
centre, rear, port wing and   starboard wing fuel
tanks respectively, in the order given
21. Oil pressure gauge

22. Fuel balancing indicator
White – Nose heavy; Black – Normal
23. Fuel balancing re-trim switch
    Retrim – Nose heavy
    Auto
    Retrim – Tail heavy

24. Fuel balancing indicator
White – Tail heavy; Black – Normal
25. Fuel flow meter
26. Jet pipe temperature gauge
28. Engine speed indicator
30. Fuel master switch

    On – Up; Off – Down
31. Ignition isolation switch
    On – Up; Off – Down
32. Starter master switch
    On – Up

Here is a shot of the lower section of the instrument panel in the F Mk 7 cockpit section with the BDAC

This is the port upper corner of the instrument panel in the F Mk 7 cockpit section with the BDAC

This is the starboard upper corner of the instrument panel in the BDAC F Mk 7 cockpit section

This is the port sidewall in Swift F Mk 4 WK275 (©Jet Art Aviation Ltd)

Here you can see further aft on the port sidewall in Swift F Mk 4 WK275
(©Jet Art Aviation Ltd)

There is not much to see on the starboard
sidewall of F Mk 4 WK275, although its all original
(©Jet Art Aviation Ltd)

An overall view of the somewhat stripped
port sidewall in the RAF Museum
FR Mk 5 WK281

An overall view of the starboard sidewall in the FR Mk 5 (WK281)
owned by the RAF Museum

This is the port sidewall in the BDAC F Mk 7 nose section

Overall top-down view of the port side console in
the BDAC F Mk 7 nose section

Overall view of the starboard sidewall in the BDAC F Mk 7

Overall port side view of this superbly restored
Martin-Baker Mk 2G ejection seat
(©Jet Art Aviation Ltd)

Here is the starboard side of the superbly restored
Martin-Baker Mk 2G ejection seat
(©Jet Art Aviation Ltd)

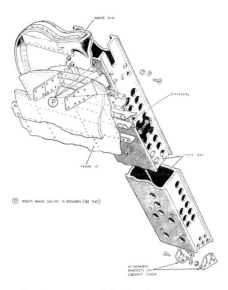

Ejection seat, removal of guide rail (©Crown Copyright)

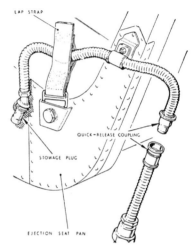

Ejection seat, release of
anti-g coupling
(©Crown Copyright)

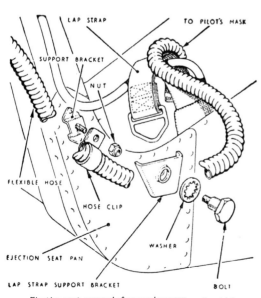

Ejection seat, detail of emergency controls (©Crown Copyright)

Ejection seat, removal of oxygen hose (©Crown Copyright)

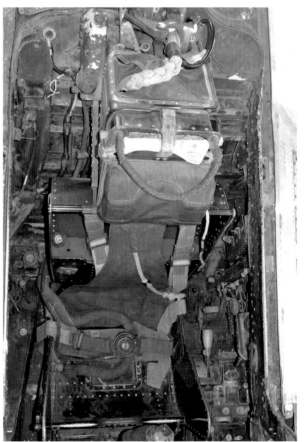

A top-down view of the Martin-Baker Mk 2G seat in F Mk 4 WK275
(©Jet Art Aviation Ltd)

Overall shot showing the base of the control column and the rudder pedals in the F Mk 7 cockpit with the BDAC

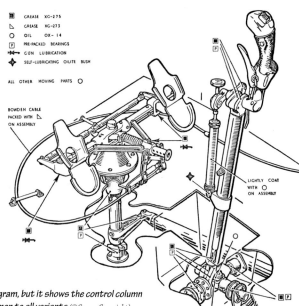

This is a lubrication diagram, but it shows the control column and rudder bar common to all variants *(©Crown Copyright)*

There is not much alongside the seat on either side, so just to prove it, this is a look down into that area on the port side of the F Mk 7 with the BDAC

While this is the area alongside/behind the starboard side of the seat in the BDAC F Mk 7

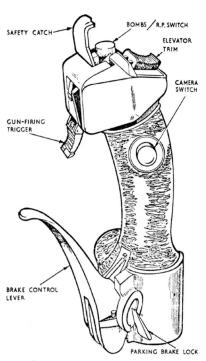

The control column handgrip, as used in all variants *(©Crown Copyright)*

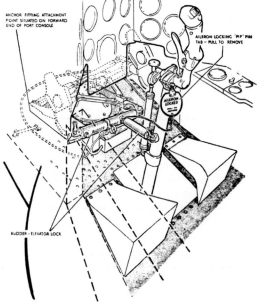

Flying control locks diagram *(©Crown Copyright)*

Although not a good photo (now some 20+ years old!), it does show the rudder pedals in the RAF Museum FR Mk 5, as well as the remains of the locking bar seen in the previous diagram

1.2 Nose, Canopy & Intakes

Here is the nose of the Type 510 (VV106) in its first form, with the blunt tip

This montage shows the revisions to the nose of the Type 510 (VV106), now fitted with a pointed profile and in-built pitot

The nose profile of the Type 535 (VV119) remained the same throughout its life and was much extended in comparison with the Type 510

The production F Mk 1 had a revised nose profile in comparison with the prototypes, it was similar to the Type 541's but had no pitot (this was on the wing) and incorporated a port for the gun camera on the port side, as seen here on WK205

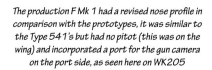

Here is a closer look at the nose cap and pitot fitted to WJ965, as you can see the latter has a step in its length

The nose shape of the 1st and 2nd pre-production Swifts (Type 541 WJ960 and 965) was narrower and had an integral pitot tube; this photo shows WJ960

This close-up under the nose of an F Mk 1 shows how short the tip was and its termination in comparison with the front of the nose wheel bay/door. The cone is painted black, but it is not a composite material, it was still aluminium

The nose profile of the F Mks 2, 3 and 4 was unchanged, as seen here with this close-up from an image of WK198, which was built as an F Mk 1 and converted to become the prototype for the F Mk 4 series

An overall shot of the nose of F Mk 4 WK275 when being delivered to Jet Art Aviation for restoration, note the intake on the top (©Jet Art Aviation Ltd)

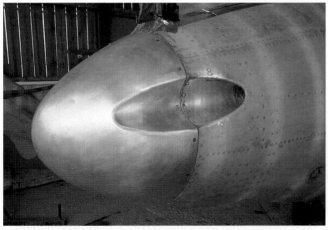

Here is the nose of F Mk 4 WK275 after refurbishment, you can see the camera gun port in the side, plus the fact the whole unit is made of aluminium
(©Jet Art Aviation Ltd)

Here with the nose cap off and the rest painted, you can see the overall shape of the F Mk 4 WK275's nose, as well as the intake on top (©Jet Art Aviation Ltd)

The nose of the FR Mk 5 was revised, with the side port removed and a lens installed in the extreme tip, with its own cover. This montaged image shows this, with the cover closed on the left and open on the right

The overall profile of the FR Mk 5 nose was revised, projecting a lot further forwards than the F Mks 1 to 4, and thus having a more pronounced taper with a smaller nose cap

The F Mk 7 nose is silly, being much longer than all previous versions, with a rounder cross-section in comparison with the FR Mk 5, as proven by the edge of the nose cap, which is almost completely round

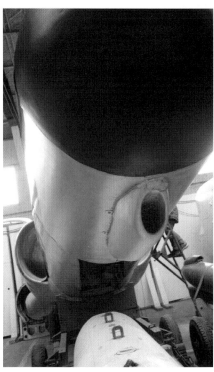

The intake seen on the top of the F Mk 4 and removed on the FR Mk 5, was present once again on the F Mk 7, but this time it went under the nose, as the extended profile allowed it to be fitted between the front of the nose wheel well and the nose cap

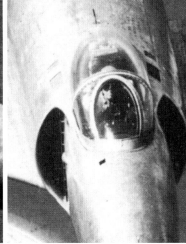

The canopy of the Type 510, VV106, was very much Attacker in overall shape, as show here in this montage of images taken from the front and side

The canopy of the Type 535 VV119 was much heavier with substantial framework as seen in these two images

This is the second pre-production Swift WJ965 and you can see that the canopy is similar to VV119, but has less pronounced framework at the back of the sliding section

These two shots show early production F Mk 1s WK194 at the top and WK198 at the bottom and you can see that the canopy has been revised once again, going back to the heavy framework of the Type 535

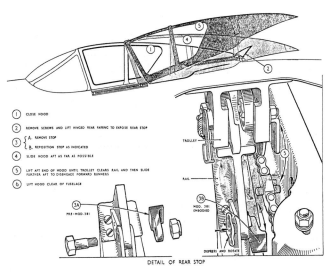

This diagram shows the rear stop on the canopy of the F Mks 1 and 2
(©Crown Copyright)

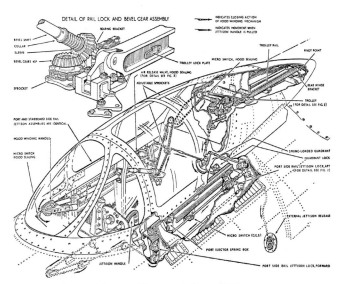

An overall diagram of the hood winding and jettison system for the F Mks 1 and 2 (©Crown Copyright)

The canopy of the F Mk 3 was unchanged from the F Mks 1 or 2, as proved by this close-up of WK247

Now the F Mk 4 actually had two types of canopy installed, this image of WK273 at Farborough clearly shows it with the same heavy-framed type used on the F Mks 1 to 3 and this applies to most of them, as there weren't many

However, F Mk 4 WK275 remained in existence for a long time and it gained a clear canopy as used on the FR Mk 5 and seen here in this image of it at Hatfield in the 1960s *(©Jet Art Aviation)*

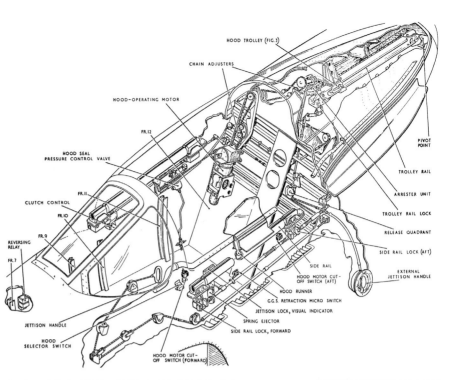

What makes things even more confusing is that the official manual for the F Mk 3 and F Mk 4 only show the later style canopy, as seen here in the winding and jettison diagram? This is probably due to the fact that the F Mks 3 and 4 never technically entered RAF service, those of the latter mark that did were converted to FR Mk 5s by that stage; this diagram therefore serves for the FR Mk 5 canopy as well *(©Crown Copyright)*

If you want to know what is underneath the canopy and directly behind the seat, this is a shot of that area on F Mk 4 WK275 during restoration
(©Jet Art Aviation Ltd)

Here you can see the relationship between the upper decking under the canopy and the rear cockpit bulkhead/seat rails. Again this is F Mk 4 WK275 during restoration *(©Jet Art Aviation Ltd)*

This is the actual canopy itself from F Mk 4 WK275, showing you the shape of the framework and the cover that is built inside the aftmost section
(©Jet Art Aviation Ltd)

The F Mk 7 had the same canopy as the FR Mk 5, as seen here on the BDAC cockpit section

A quick close-up of the 'clear' canopy used on the FR Mk 5, as seen here on the RAF Museum example at Tangmere *(©P. Mills)*

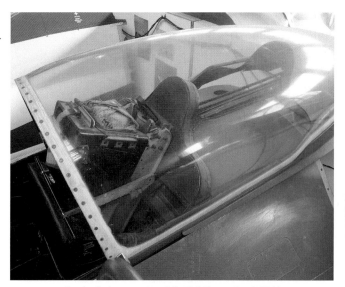

Here is the front section of the F Mk 7 canopy with BDAC

This is the rear section of the BDAC F Mk 7 canopy, through which you can see the chains that allow it to be wound in and out

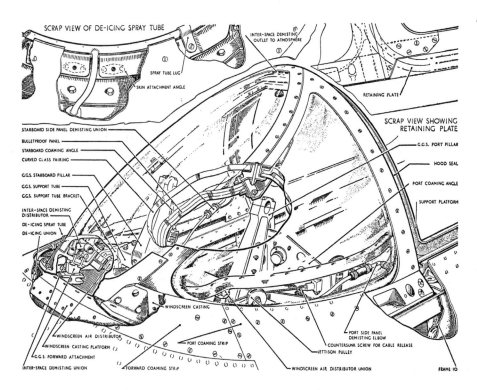

SCRAP VIEW OF DE-ICING SPRAY TUBE

SPRAY TUBE LUG

SKIN ATTACHMENT ANGLE

INTER-SPACE DEMISTING OUTLET TO ATMOSPHERE

RETAINING PLATE

SCRAP VIEW SHOWING RETAINING PLATE

STARBOARD SIDE PANEL DEMISTING UNION
BULLETPROOF PANEL
STARBOARD COAMING ANGLE
CURVED GLASS FAIRING
G.G.S. STARBOARD PILLAR
G.G.S. SUPPORT TUBE
G.G.S. SUPPORT TUBE BRACKET
INTER-SPACE DEMISTING DISTRIBUTOR
DE-ICING SPRAY TUBE
DE-ICING UNION

G.G.S. PORT PILLAR
HOOD SEAL
PORT COAMING ANGLE
SUPPORT PLATFORM

WINDSCREEN CASTING

WINDSCREEN AIR DISTRIBUTOR
WINDSCREEN CASTING PLATFORM
G.G.S. FORWARD ATTACHMENT
INTER-SPACE DEMISTING UNION
PORT COAMING STRIP
FORWARD COAMING STRIP

PORT SIDE PANEL DEMISTING ELBOW
COUNTERSUNK SCREW FOR CABLE RELEASE
JETTISON PULLEY
WINDSCREEN AIR DISTRIBUTOR UNION
FRAME 10

This diagram from the F Mks 3 and 4 manual gives cross-sections through the various frames of the windscreen, showing their construction (©Crown Copyright)

This diagram shows the windscreen assembly from the F Mks 1 and 2, but it applies to all variants (©Crown Copyright)

Here you can see the glass and frames along with all the seals on the F Mk 4 WK275 during restoration (©Jet Art Aviation Ltd)

Here is WK275's canopy with all the outer skins in place (©Jet Art Aviation Ltd)

This is the upper edge of the windscreen of the F Mk 7 with the BDAC and you can see the large lip required to seal the main hood. The white along the edges you can see is a sealant inside the glass

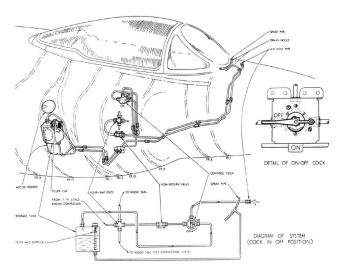

All variants used this simple de-icer system for the windscreen *(©Crown Copyright)*

Inside the windscreen was this pipe that wound around inside, it had small holes to allow warm air to go up inside the side and front panels, plus a main outlet at either side to heat the cockpit canopy. This is the BDAC F Mk 7, but all machines are similar

The Type 535 (VV119) had much deeper intakes, but again no vents ahead of them as would be seen with later variants

The intakes on the Type 510 (VV106) were simple, quite shallow and had no boundary vents ahead of them. There was a slight gap just inside the intakes themselves, up against the fuselage, but you can't see it here due to the fitment of FOD guards

The intakes on the pre-production Type 541s WJ960 and WJ965 were shallower than VV119's but deeper than VV106's

This close-up of the intakes in F Mk 1 WK212 shows the revised profile of the production intakes plus the vents just ahead of them

The F Mk 4 had the same basic shape as the F Mks 1 to 3, although both the F Mks 3 and 4 manuals list de-icing for the intakes, so this may be around the lip. This photos shows the intakes on F Mk 4 WK275 during restoration, with the lip edges masked off (©Jet Art Aviation Ltd)

The FR Mk 5 intakes look pretty much like those in all the other production machines, as seen here on the RAF Museum example (WK281) at Tangmere
(©R. Mills)

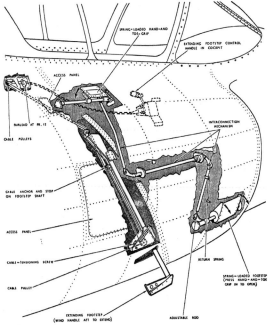

The starboard intake also housed the access step as seen in this official diagram (©Crown Copyright)

The air bleeds off the intakes vents through louvers above and below each intake, this shows the upper ones on the port side of the BDAC F Mk 7

This close-up from an image of F Mk 1 WK212, clearly shows how the access step drops down and the step opens in the bottom of the intake flaring

A detailed shot of the intakes on the F Mk 7 cockpit section with the BDAC, with the vents ahead of them visible, plus the boundary bleed splitter in the intake itself [on the fuselage side]

A closer look alongside the nose into the intakes on the BDAC F Mk 7, looking into the vents ahead of the intakes and the separator inside the intake itself to bleed off air

1.3 Mid and Rear Fuselage

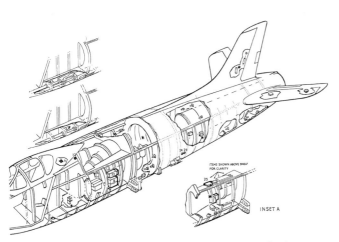

This diagram shows the location of the main equipment within the fuselage of the F Mks 1 and 2 *(©Crown Copyright)*

Underside shot of the fuselage of F Mk 4 WK275 as it is unloaded to start its restoration *(©Jet Art Aviation Ltd)*

Here is F Mk 4 WK275 under cover, with all the paint stripped and repairs completed *(©Jet Art Aviation Ltd)*

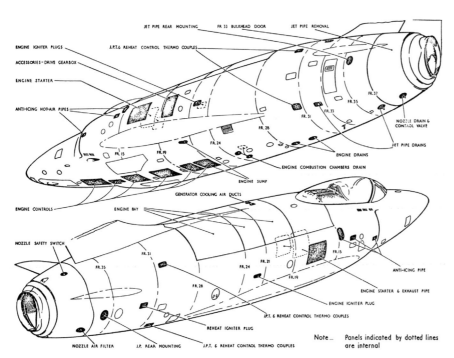

Doors 'A' and 'B' must be closed manually prior to take-off and opened manually after landing

Doors 'C' and 'D' are automatically retained in a closed position by airflow during flight

These are the ground running air outlets on the aft dorsal spine of the F Mks 3 and 4 *(©Crown Copyright)*

This diagram shows all the doors and access panels in the fuselage undersides for the F Mks 3 and 4
(©Crown Copyright)

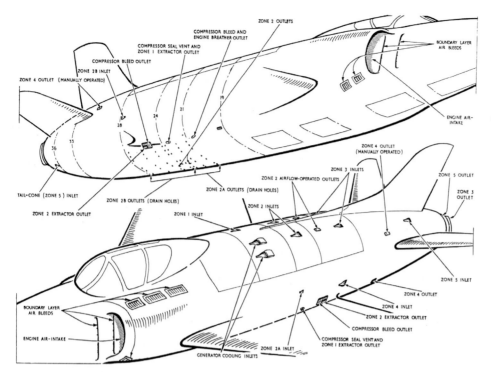

The air inlets and outlets
on the F Mk 3 fuselage
(©Crown Copyright)

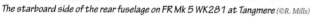

The starboard side of the rear fuselage on FR Mk 5 WK281 at Tangmere (©R. Mills)

The port side of the rear fuselage of FR Mk 5 WK281 (©R. Mills)

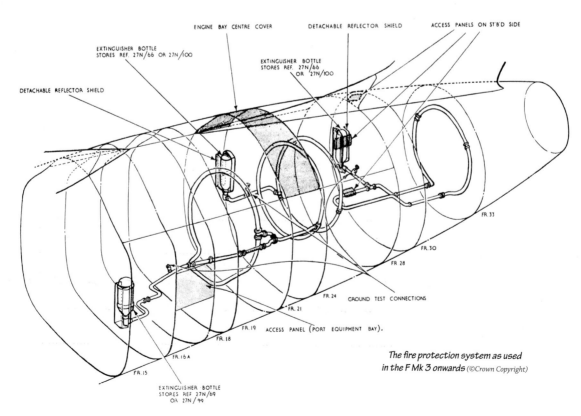

The fire protection system as used
in the F Mk 3 onwards (©Crown Copyright)

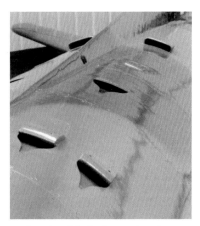

Up on top of the fuselage you have these air scoops relating to the generator cooling ducts and various air intakes to different regions of the engine bay

In this shot of the lower port fuselage on FR Mk 5 WK281 you can see some of the various intakes and things like the compressor outlets that were shown on the inlets and outlets diagram earlier in this section (©R. Mills)

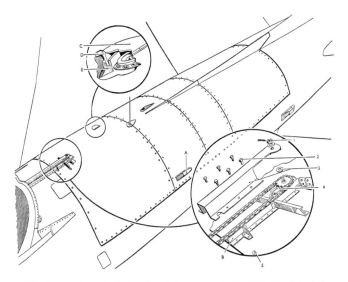

This diagram shows the tank and engine bay covers for the F Mks 1 and 2, which you can see are less complex that later variants, with far fewer intakes etc. (©Crown Copyright)

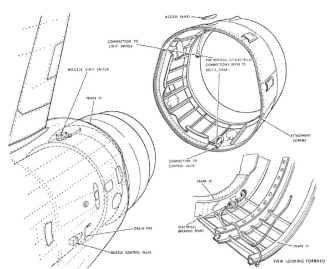

This diagram shows how the tail cone can be removed and applies to the F Mk 3 through to the F Mk 7 (©Crown Copyright)

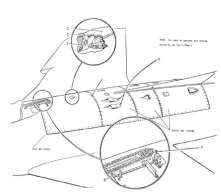

Engine bay and tank cover removal for the F Mk 7, which looks to be identical to that for the FR Mk 5 (©Crown Copyright)

Access doors and panels on the fuselage of the F Mk 7 (©Crown Copyright)

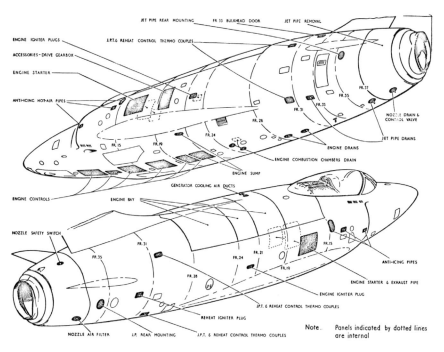

Note: Panels indicated by dotted lines are internal

1.4 Access Panels

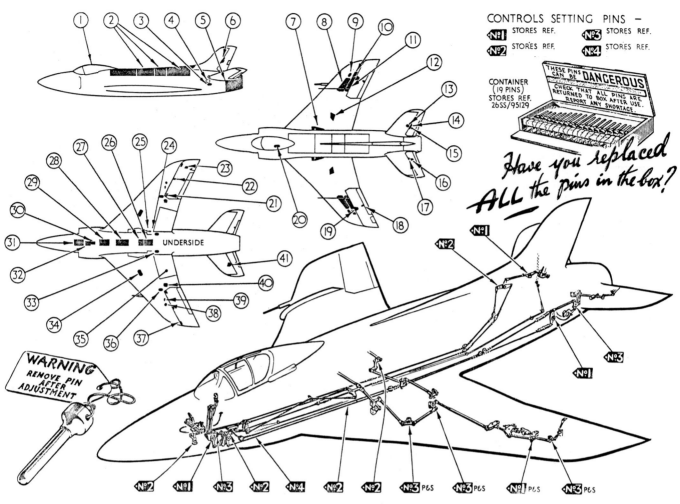

CONTROLS SETTING PINS –

№1 STORES REF.   №3 STORES REF.
№2 STORES REF.   №4 STORES REF.

CONTAINER (19 PINS) STORES REF. 26SS/95129

THESE PINS CAN BE **DANGEROUS**
CHECK THAT ALL PINS ARE RETURNED TO BOX AFTER USE. REPORT ANY SHORTAGE.

Have you replaced ALL the pins in the box?

UNDERSIDE

WARNING REMOVE PIN AFTER ADJUSTMENT

Swift F Mks 1, 2 & 3 – Location of access panels and setting pins (©Crown Copyright)

Key

1. Cockpit hood
2. Controls aft of frame 19 (engine removed)
3. Inspection – tension compensators (port only)
4. Rudder controls (starboard only)
5. Rudder and elevator controls (tail cone and jet pipe removed)
6. Rudder trim actuator and linkage
7. Aileron levers on main spar (port and starboard)
8. Hydrobooster (port and starboard)
9. Aileron bell crank – outboard
10. Aileron connecting rod
11. Hydromooster – removal
12. Ailerons – inboard rear bellcrank
13. Chain connections – emergency elevator trim
14. Elevator trim linkage
15. Elevator trim tab connecting rod
16. Elevator spring tab connecting rod
17. Elevator spring tab damper
18. Aileron balance tab connecting rod
19. Aileron connecting rod
20. Elevator emergency trim controls under cockpit floor (sealed)
21. Aileron inboard hinge
22. Aileron centre hinge and balance tab connecting rod
23. Aileron trim tab connecting rod
24. Flaps interconnection sliding seals (wing fillet removed)
25. Aileron levers on main spar (wing fillet removed)
26. Rudder tension rods
27. Aileron three-armed lever
28. Aileron chains and tension rods: rudder tension compensators
29. Tension rods and fairleads
30. Aileron and rudder levers aft of frame 11
31. Servodyne and controls under cockpit floor
32. Servodyne and elevator emergency trim chain
33. Flaps interconnection levers
34. Aileron inboard forward bell crank
35. Flaps connections when flaps down
36. Aileron inboard hinge
37. Aileron outboard hinge
38. Hydrobooster – Lost motion linkage
39. Hydrobooster control valve
40. Aileron inboard hinge

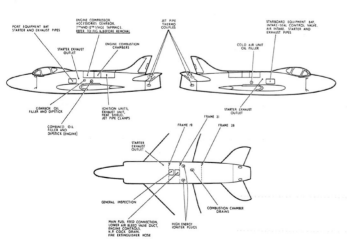

PORT EQUIPMENT BAY. STARTER AND EXHAUST PIPES

ENGINE COMPRESSOR ACCESSORIES GEARBOX. 7ᵀᴴ AND 12ᵀᴴ STAGE TAPPINGS. REFER TO FIG. II BEFORE REMOVAL.

STARTER EXHAUST OUTLET

ENGINE COMBUSTION CHAMBERS

JET PIPE THERMO COUPLES

STARBOARD EQUIPMENT BAY. INTAKE-SEAL CONTROL VALVE, AIR INTAKE, STARTER AND EXHAUST PIPES

COLD AIR UNIT OIL FILLER

GEARBOX OIL FILLER AND DIPSTICK

COMBINED OIL FILLER AND DIPSTICK (ENGINE)

IGNITION UNITS, EXHAUST UNIT, HEAT SHIELD, JET PIPE CLAMPS

STARTER EXHAUST OUTLET

FRAME 21

FRAME 19   FRAME 28

STARTER EXHAUST OUTLET

GENERAL INSPECTION

COMBUSTION CHAMBER DRAINS

MAIN FUEL FEED CONNECTION, LOWER AIR BLEED VALVE DUCT, ENGINE CONTROLS, H.P. COCK DRAIN, FIRE EXTINGUISHER HOSE

HIGH ENERGY IGNITER PLUGS

This diagram shows all the access panels relating to the engine system and applies to the F Mk 1 through F Mk 3 (©Crown Copyright)

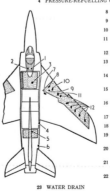

1 FORWARD TANK FILLER CAP
2 FUEL LEVEL FLOAT SWITCH
3 CENTRE TANK FILLER CAP
4 PRESSURE-REFUELLING COUPLING
5 REAR TANK FILLER CAP
6 REHEAT MAIN FUEL CONNECTION TO JET PIPE
7 INBOARD BOOSTER PUMP CONNECTIONS
8 INBOARD BOOSTER PUMP REMOVAL
9 INBOARD TANK FILLER CAP
10 HAND HOLE (INSPECTION)
11 OUTBOARD TANK FILLER CAP AND BOOSTER PUMP REMOVAL
12 HAND HOLES (INSPECTION)
13 FORWARD TANK BOOSTER PUMP-FUEL AND WATER DRAINS
14 CENTRE TANK BOOSTER PUMP AND FUEL DRAIN
15 FUSELAGE SIDE TANK BOOSTER PUMP AND FUEL DRAIN
16 FUEL COLLECTOR BOX AND GROUND-TEST CONNECTIONS
17 FUEL FEED CONNECTION TO ENGINE
18 FUEL TRAP AND REHEAT PUMP
19 REAR TANK FUEL AND WATER DRAINS-REHEAT PUMP
20 REHEAT PILOT FUEL PIPE CONNECTION
21 REAR TANK BALANCE PIPE CONNECTION
22 REAR TANK BOOSTER PUMP
23 WATER DRAIN
24 FUEL DRAIN
25 PRESSURE-REFUELLING LINES
26 WATER DRAIN
27 FUEL DRAIN
28 OUTBOARD BOOSTER PUMP CONNECTIONS
29 HAND HOLES (INSPECTION)

Access panels, this diagram is from the F Mk 7 manual but it also applies to the FR Mk 5 (©Crown Copyright)

2.1 Undercarriage – Main

This head-on view of the main undercarriage of the Type 510 VV106, shows the split main doors, which were only used on this prototype

This view underneath VV106 as it comes in to land better illustrates the two-part main undercarriage doors used by the type

This is VV119 and as you can see it has a tricycle undercarriage that is pretty similar to the production Swifts, the oleo legs are of a slightly different design though

This shows the first pre-production Swift, WJ960, which has the same overall units as VV119 although the main wheel hubs are larger

This is the second pre-production Swift WJ965, and you can see the units and doors are similar to the production machines, plus you can also see the style/size of the main wheel hubs

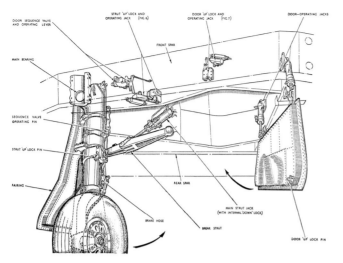

This diagram shows the overall main undercarriage system
as used for all variants of the Swift *(©Crown Copyright)*

This image shows the oleo leg and brakes, with the hub/wheel removed,
on the F Mk 4 WK275 currently being restored *(©Jet Art Aviation Ltd)*

An overall shot of the port undercarriage unit on FR Mk 5 WK281
at Tangmere *(©R. Mills)*

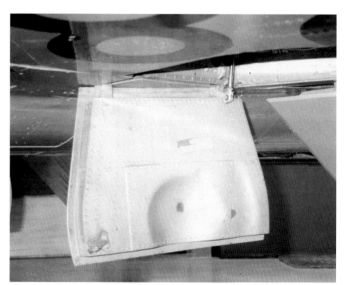

This is the inner undercarriage door on FR Mk 5 WK281,
but it was the same for all variants of the Swift *(©R. Mills)*

2.2 Undercarriage – Tail bumper

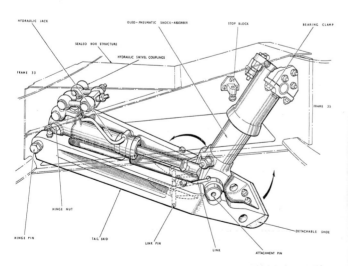

Although the Type 510 and 535 prototypes had the twin tailwheel unit, the
two pre-production machines plus all F Mks 1 and 2 had this tail bumper unit
installed. We do not believe this was used with later versions, as it is not included
in their manuals *(©Crown Copyright)*

This is the second pre-production Swift (Type 541) WJ965 and
you can see the tail bumper unit extended

2.3 Undercarriage – Nose

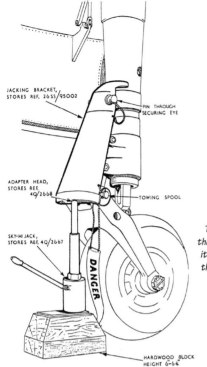

JACKING BRACKET, STORES REF. 26S5/95002

PIN THROUGH SECURING EYE

ADAPTER HEAD, STORES REF. 4G/2668

TOWING SPOOL

SKY-HI JACK, STORES REF. 4G/2667

DANGER

HARDWOOD BLOCK HEIGHT 6-6¾

This is the nose oleo top mounting strut and it applies to all variants (©Crown Copyright)

This diagram shows how the nose wheel is jacked and it applies to all versions of the Swift (©Crown Copyright)

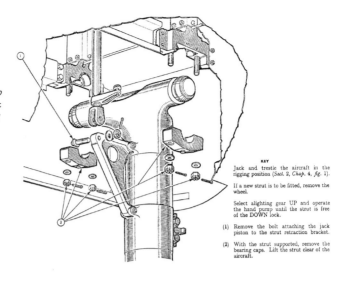

KEY

Jack and trestle the aircraft in the rigging position (*Sect. 2, Chap. 4, fig. 1*).

If a new strut is to be fitted, remove the wheel.

Select alighting gear UP and operate the hand pump until the strut is free of the DOWN lock.

(1) Remove the bolt attaching the jack piston to the strut retraction bracket.

(2) With the strut supported, remove the bearing caps. Lift the strut clear of the aircraft.

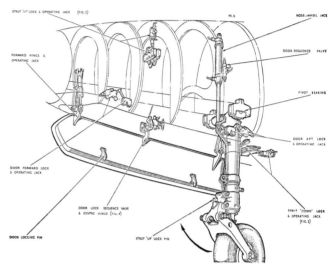

STRUT 'UP' LOCK & OPERATING JACK (FIG. 3)

FR. 6

NOSE-WHEEL JACK

FORWARD HINGE & OPERATING JACK

DOOR SEQUENCE VALVE

PIVOT BEARING

DOOR FORWARD LOCK & OPERATING JACK

DOOR AFT LOCK & OPERATING JACK

DOOR LOCK SEQUENCE VALVE & CENTRE HINGE (FIG.4)

DOOR LOCKING PIN

STRUT 'UP' LOCK PIN

STRUT 'DOWN' LOCK & OPERATING JACK (FIG. 2)

This diagram from the F Mks 1 and 2 manual shows the nose wheel unit, but this also applies to the F Mk 3 and F Mk 4 (©Crown Copyright)

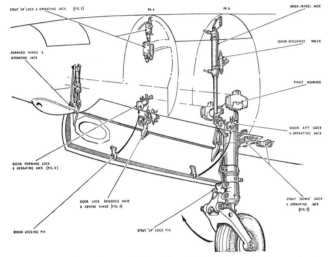

STRUT 'UP' LOCK & OPERATING JACK (FIG. 3)

FR. 4

FR. 6

NOSE-WHEEL JACK

FORWARD HINGE & OPERATING JACK

DOOR SEQUENCE VALVE

PIVOT BEARING

DOOR AFT LOCK & OPERATING JACK

DOOR FORWARD LOCK & OPERATING JACK (FIG.5)

DOOR LOCK SEQUENCE VALVE & CENTRE HINGE (FIG.4)

DOOR LOCKING PIN

STRUT 'UP' LOCK PIN

STRUT 'DOWN' LOCK & OPERATING JACK (FIG. 2)

This diagram shows the nose wheel unit for the F Mk 7, note the shortened and revised door etc. that only applies to this variant (©Crown Copyright)

The nose wheel well in the F Mk 7 cockpit section with the BDAC is pretty trashed and devoid of a lot of fittings, but it still makes a useful source of information as far as the bulkheads etc. go

A quick look up into the nose wheel well of FR Mk 5 WK281 at Tangmere (©R. Mills)

3.1 Tailplane

This close-up shows the tailplanes fitted to the Type 510 VV106

This montage of images shows the tailplane fitted to the Type 535 VV119

This close-up of the tail of F Mk 3 WK247 shows the vortex generators on the starboard tailplane adopted to try and cure handling problems

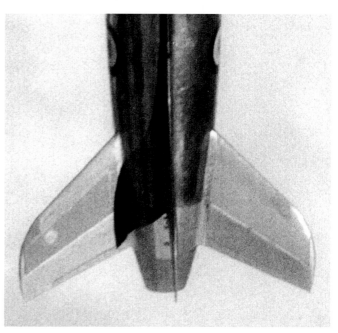

A nice clear top-down view of the tail on the second pre-production Swift (Type 541) WJ965

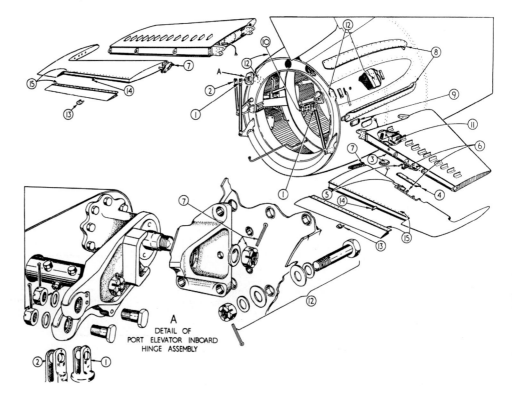

This diagram of the elevators and tailplane from the F Mk 3 manual shows the vortex generators on both tailplanes, where period images show them only on the starboard. Note the mass balance extension to the elevator tip, which actually only applies to the F Mks 1 and 2 (©Crown Copyright)

A
DETAIL OF
PORT ELEVATOR INBOARD
HINGE ASSEMBLY

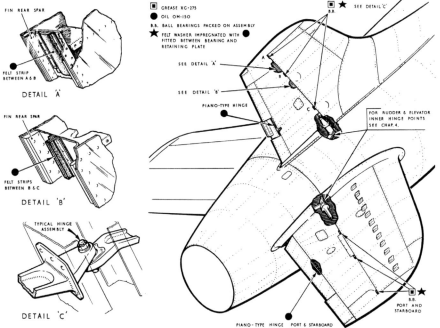

GREASE XG-275
OIL OM-150
B.B. BALL BEARINGS PACKED ON ASSEMBLY
FELT WASHER IMPREGNATED WITH FITTED BETWEEN BEARING AND RETAINING PLATE

FIN REAR SPAR

FELT STRIP BETWEEN A & B

DETAIL 'A'

FIN REAR SPAR

FELT STRIPS BETWEEN B & C

DETAIL 'B'

TYPICAL HINGE ASSEMBLY

DETAIL 'C'

SEE DETAIL 'A'
SEE DETAIL 'B'
PIANO-TYPE HINGE
SEE DETAIL 'C'
B.B.
FOR RUDDER & ELEVATOR INNER HINGE POINTS SEE CHAP. 4.
B.B. PORT AND STARBOARD
PIANO-TYPE HINGE PORT & STARBOARD

Here you can see the mass balance on the tip of the elevators on F Mk 1 WK209, this also applies to the F Mks 2 and 3. Note that the first aerodynamic prototype for the FR Mk 5 (WK200) retained these, as it was originally an F Mk 1 airframe

When you look at the lubrication diagram for the tail of the F Mk 3, however, it clearly shows the vortex generators on the starboard tailplane only (©Crown Copyright)

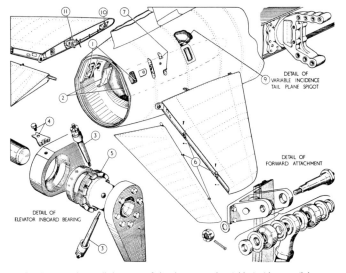

DETAIL OF VARIABLE INCIDENCE TAIL PLANE SPIGOT
DETAIL OF FORWARD ATTACHMENT
DETAIL OF ELEVATOR INBOARD BEARING

This diagram shows all elements of the elevator and variable-incidence tailplane on the F Mk 4; the FR Mk 5 and F Mk 7 are the same (©Crown Copyright)

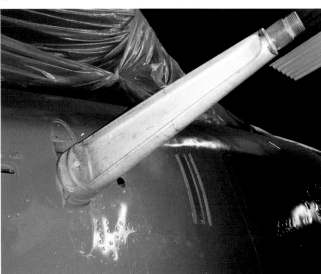

This is the variable-incidence tailplane mounting spigot of Mk 4 WK275, this is not shown in the diagram of this area (©Jet Art Aviation Ltd)

Here are the give-away slots at the front of the tailplane that identify the variable-incidence unit, this is FR Mk 5 WK281 at Tangmere (©R. Mills)

Here is a close-up of the tailplane of F Mk 7 XF124, you can see the variable-incidence unit, plus the revised profile of the elevator

3.2 Vertical Fin & Rudder

This is the vertical tail and rudder of the Type 510, VV106 in its original form, note the pitot on the leading edge

Here is the original vertical tail and rudder on the Type 535 VV119, when the extension was not fitted

This is the first pre-production F Mk 1 (Type 541) WJ960 and you can see that it too had the fin extension installed plus, uniquely, it had a pitot on the top leading edge *(©Vickers)*

This is the tail of VV119 when the extension was fitted on the dorsal spine

Here you can see the tails of a number of early machines, including the Type 535 VV119, the second pre-production F Mk 1 (Type 541) WJ965 and the first two production machines WK194 and WK195, all of which have the fin extension installed. Note the blister fitted on the starboard side of the vertical fin of WJ965
(©Vickers)

An overall view of the vertical tail and rudder on one of the early production machines. Note the split of the trim tabs, bottom rudder hinge line and the fact that this particular aircraft has the variable-incidence tailplane fitted

The vertical tail and rudder of an early production F Mk 1, proving that the main production batch had the fixed tailplanes fitted

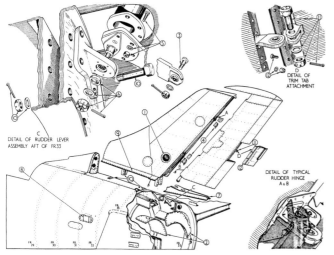

This diagram shows all the elements of the vertical fin and rudder for the F Mk 3 (©Crown Copyright)

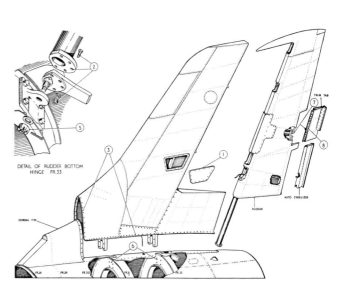

Here you can see all elements of the vertical fin and rudder on the F Mk 4, note how these vary slightly from the F Mk 3 seen previously. The F Mks 5 and 7 used the same assembly (©Crown Copyright)

Overall image of the fin and rudder of FR Mk 5 WK281 at Tangmere (©R. Mills)

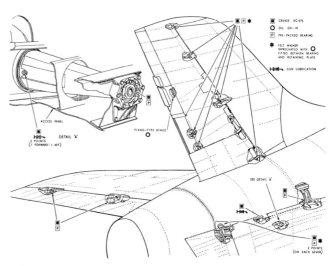

This diagram, which shows the lubrication points on the fin and tailplanes of the F Mk 7, also shows the revised hinge lines of the rudder etc. (©Crown Copyright)

4.1 Controls & Control Surfaces

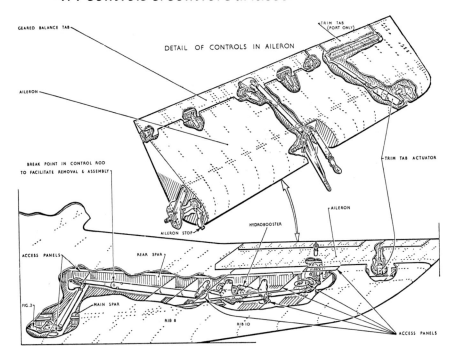

DETAIL OF CONTROLS IN AILERON

GEARED BALANCE TAB

TRIM TAB (PORT ONLY)

AILERON

BREAK POINT IN CONTROL ROD TO FACILITATE REMOVAL & ASSEMBLY

TRIM TAB ACTUATOR

This diagram shows the controls in the mainplane of the F Mks 1 and 2
(©Crown Copyright)

AILERON STOP

HYDROBOOSTER

AILERON

ACCESS PANELS

REAR SPAR

FIG.2

MAIN SPAR

RIB 8

RIB 10

ACCESS PANELS

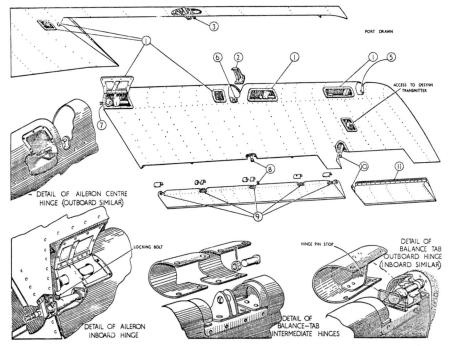

PORT DRAWN

ACCESS TO DESYNN TRANSMITTER

This diagram shows the aileron and trim tabs removal and it applies to all variants of the Swift *(©Crown Copyright)*

DETAIL OF AILERON CENTRE HINGE (OUTBOARD SIMILAR)

LOCKING BOLT

HINGE PIN STOP

DETAIL OF BALANCE TAB OUTBOARD HINGE (INBOARD SIMILAR)

DETAIL OF AILERON INBOARD HINGE

DETAIL OF BALANCE-TAB INTERMEDIATE HINGES

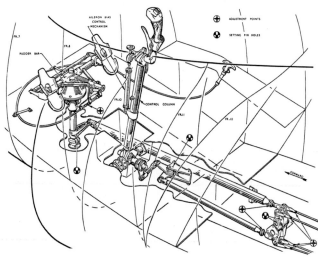

AILERON BIAS CONTROL MECHANISM

ADJUSTMENT POINTS

SETTING PIN HOLES

FR.7

FR.4

RUDDER BAR

FR.10

CONTROL COLUMN

FR.11

FR.12

FORWARD

This diagram shows the linkage for the rudder and ailerons in the cockpit and it applies to all variants of the Swift *(©Crown Copyright)*

This close-up of a shot of FR Mk 5 XD907 helps to show the revised profile of the wing inboard of the aileron hinge line, this applies to all variants

5.1 Wings

Here is the underside of the wing on VV106 (Type 510),
showing the flaps deployed

This is a close-up of the top surface of the Type 510's (VV106) wing, showing
the overall profile and shape of the aileron etc

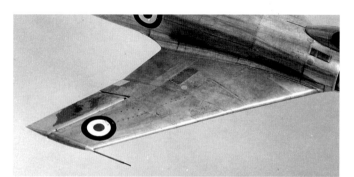

Here is a close-up of the wing of the Type 535 VV119, note the pitot
on the starboard tip and the kinked trailing edge line

This is the underside of the wing of the pre-production Swift WJ960,
it is the same as the Type 535

Overall view of the wings of the F Mk 1 WK205
with the wing fence and pitot as per WJ965

A nice plan top view of the wing of the second pre-production Swift WJ965, note
the wing fence added at 2/3rd span and the pitot added just outboard of it

This is the main spar bracket in the fuselage of F Mk 4 WK275
during restoration (©Jet Art Aviation Ltd)

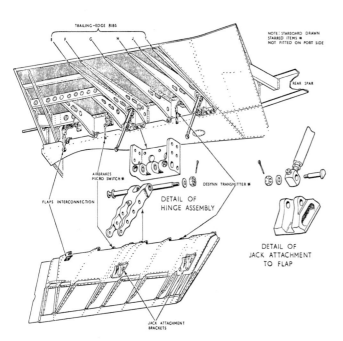

Here are all the components of the trailing edge flaps and it applies to all production versions of the Swift (©Crown Copyright)

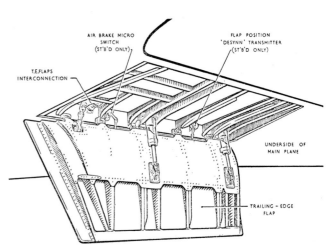

This diagram shows all elements of the trailing edge flaps, again it applies to all variants (©Crown Copyright)

Here is a photo of the trailing edge flaps on the FR Mk 5 WK281 at Tangmere (©R. Mills)

Overall view of the underside of the wing on FR Mk 5 WK303, showing the sawtooth of the leading edge and the standard tip profile

Here is a close-up of the sawtooth in the leading edge of the wing on the F Mk 7

The F Mk 7 had extended tips, as seen in this shot of XF124, note how the aileron outer edge is now within the boundary of the wing, where the F Mks 1 to 5 had this point as the tip profile (compare with above image of WK303)

6.1 Engine & Afterburner Exhaust

Here is the Avon out of F Mk 4 WK275 and now mounted in a handling trolley (©Jet Art Aviation)

This is the Avon being removed from the fuselage of F Mk 4 WK275 during the initial dismantling prior to restoration (©Jet Art Aviation Ltd)

Here is a close-up of the front section of the Avon along with the fuel cell in front of it; the front of the aircraft is at the top of this image (©Jet Art Aviation Ltd)

The prototypes had the Nene, but all production machines had the Rolls-Royce Avon, this shows the overall engine bay in F Mk 4 WK275 during strip-down prior to restoration. Note the fuel tank in the front of the compartment (©Jet Art Aviation Ltd)

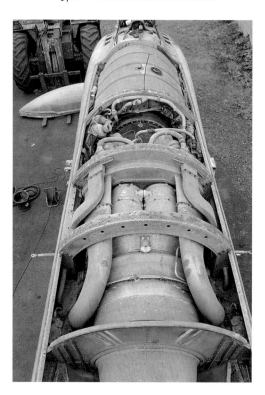

This is the engine compressor case and generators of F Mk 4 WK275 during strip-down (©Jet Art Aviation Ltd)

This is the afterburner nozzle in the back of F Mk 4 WK275 during strip-down (©Jet Art Aviation Ltd)

Here is the exhaust jet pipe removed from F Mk 4 WK275 (©Jet Art Aviation Ltd)

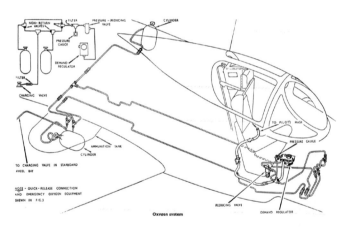

A neat view of the jet exhaust in FR Mk 5 WK296 at Farnborough in 1956 (©MOD)

The complete afterburner jet pipe from F Mk 4 WK275 (©Jet Art Aviation Ltd)

Group 7.1 Fuel & Oxygen Systems

This is the forward fuel cell in the fuselage of F Mk 4 WK275 during strip-down prior to restoration. Note that the front of the aircraft is to the bottom of the page (©Jet Art Aviation Ltd)

Note: None of the official publications for the Swift seem to cover the oil and hydraulic systems, so we have refrained from mentioning them in this section

This diagram shows the oxygen system from the F Mk 4, all other variants are similar (©Crown Copyright)

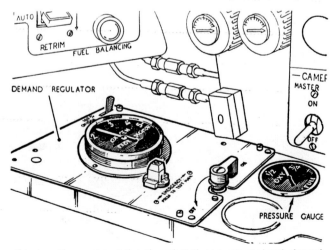

This shows the oxygen controls in the cockpit, these are situated on the front of the side console on the port side of the cockpit in all variants (©Crown Copyright)

8.1 Weapons – Armament

None of the prototypes had armament, but the Type 535 VV119 had dummy cannon fairings fitted for its display at Farnborough in 1950

Whilst the first pre-production F Mk 1 WJ960 did not have cannon fitted in the fuselage, it is stated that the second WJ965 did, so how come this clear image of the underside of that machines proves there are no gun ports, though?

Early production F Mk 1 WK198 undertook a London to Paris flight in July 1953 and as you can see from this close-up, all four cannon ports were covered over

This shot of the second pre-production airframe WJ965 clearly shows the twin cannon ports in the underside, so these must have been added at some stage of its test programme

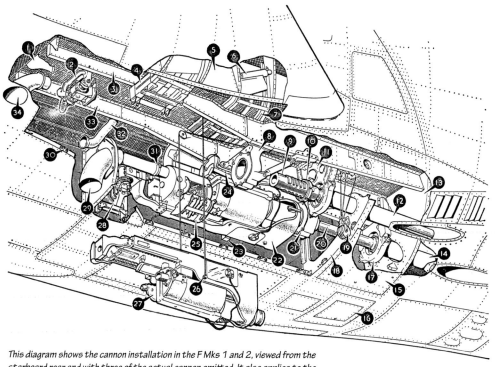

This diagram shows the cannon installation in the F Mks 1 and 2, viewed from the starboard rear and with three of the actual cannon omitted. It also applies to the F Mks 3 and 4 (©Crown Copyright)

KEY

(GUN INSTALLATION—STARBOARD)

1   REAR DIAPHRAGM
2   REAR OUTBOARD MOUNTING
3   OUTER GUN BEAM
4   OUTBOARD GUN-FEED CHUTE
5   ROOT RIB
6   FEED ROLLER
7   INBOARD GUN-FEED CHUTE
8   OUTBOARD FRONT MOUNTING
9   OUTBOARD GUN-BARREL
10 GUN BOSS NUT
11 OUTBOARD BARREL SUPPORT
12 OUTBOARD BLAST TUBE
13 FRAME 12
14 INBOARD BLAST TUBE
15 HINGED PANEL (ACCESS TO INBOARD BARREL SUPPORT)
16 SCAVENGE FLAP
17 INBOARD BARREL SUPPORT
18 FORWARD DIAPHRAGM
19 HOIST PULLEYS (fig. 20)
20 INBOARD GUN-BARREL
21 FRONT INBOARD MOUNTING
22 INBOARD GUN
23 SCAVENGE TEST SWITCH
24 INNER GUN BEAM
25 LINK CHUTE
26 CABLE ATTACHMENT TO GUN CRADLE
27 OUTBOARD GUN
28 REAR INBOARD MOUNTING
29 INBOARD CASE CHUTE
30 DOOR LATCH PLATE
31 DETACHABLE CASE CHUTE
32 PIPE FROM WATER EXTRACTOR (AIR CONDITIONING SYSTEM)
33 CENTRE GUN BEAM
34 OUTBOARD CASE CHUTE

Here you can see the four cannon ports in the fuselage underside of F Mk 3 WK247

Here is a clearer shot of the four cannon ports on the underside of F Mk 4 WK275 (©Jet Art Aviation Ltd)

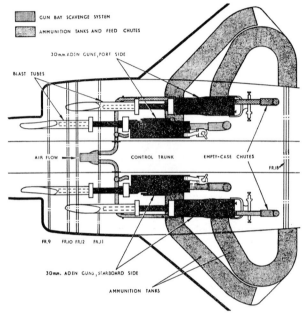

Layout of guns and ammunition tanks in the four-cannon installation, this comes from the F Mk 4 manual (©Crown Copyright)

This is the front inboard mounting for the cannon (©Crown Copyright)

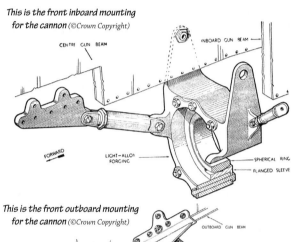

This is the front outboard mounting for the cannon (©Crown Copyright)

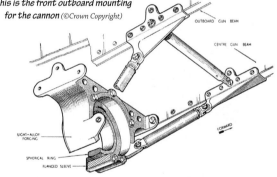

This is one of the rear mounts for the cannon (©Crown Copyright)

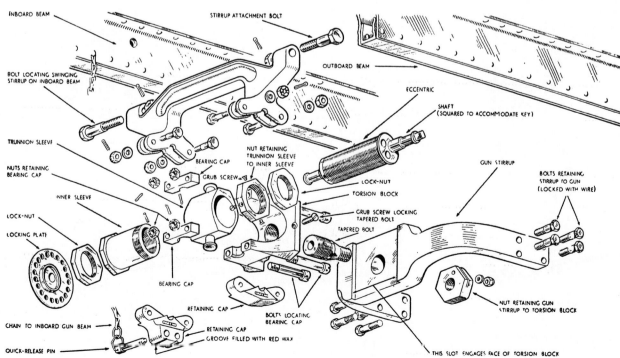

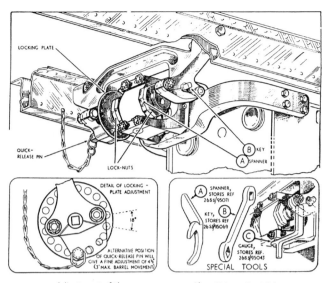

Adjustment of the rear cannon mountings (©Crown Copyright)

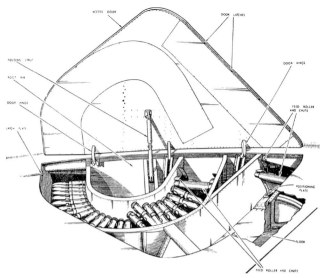

The ammunition tanks at each wing root, these apply to all variants except the F Mk 7 (©Crown Copyright)

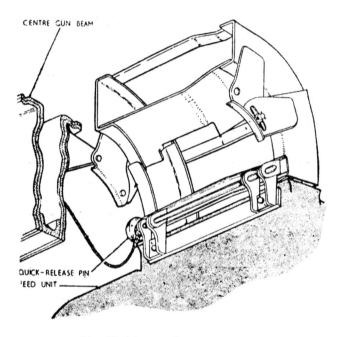

Inboard feed chute attachment (©Crown Copyright)

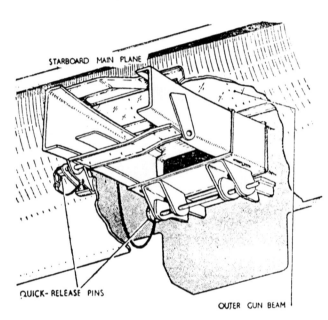

Outboard feed chute attachment (©Crown Copyright)

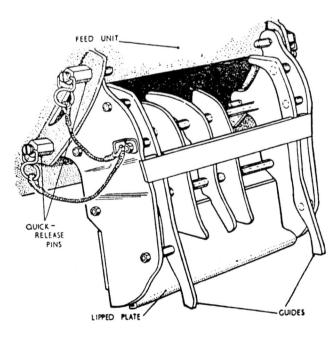

Inboard empty-case chute (©Crown Copyright)

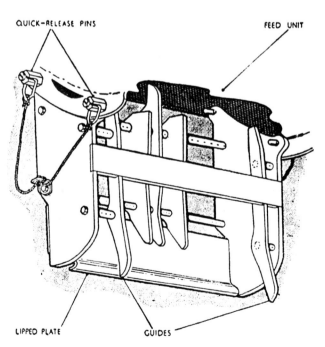

Outboard empty-case chute (©Crown Copyright)

Front view of the twin cannon ports underside the FR Mk 5

This view of the underside of an FR Mk 5 during a loop nicely shows the single cannon port

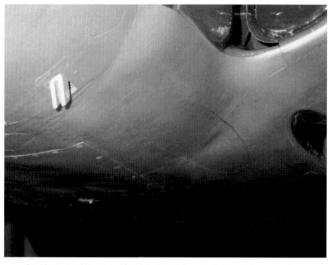

This close-up of the nose of FB Mk 5 WK281 clearly shows the covered over inboard cannon port (©R. Mills)

This is the underside of F Mk 7 XF124 showing that the series was unarmed

8.1 Weapons – Sighting

This is the bomb pylon that could be carried by all versions from the F Mk 1 through to the F Mk 4 (©Crown Copyright)

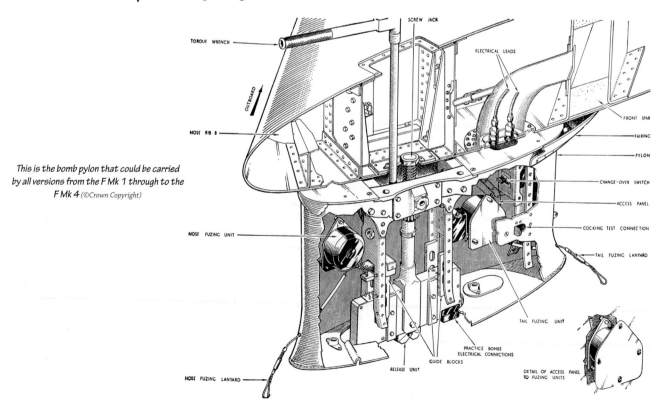

8.2 Weapons – Bombs, Rockets & Missiles

Here is a 1,000lb bomb fitted under the port wing of F Mk 4 WK273 at Farnborough in 1954

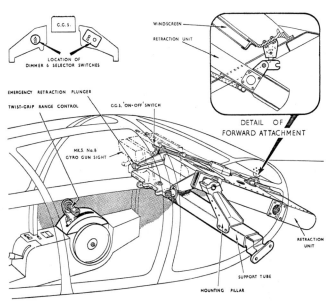

This diagram shows the installation of the Gyro Gun Sight (GGS), the Swift used the Mk 5 No 8 unit *(©Crown Copyright)*

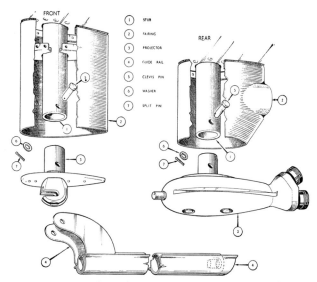

The detachable fittings for the rocket projectile rails that could be carried by the F Mk 1 to F Mk 4 *(©Crown Copyright)*

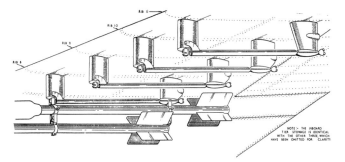

These are the rocket projectile rails used on the F Mk 1 to 4 *(©Crown Copyright)*

Here is a front view of 3in rocket projectiles in a two-tier installation under the port wing of F Mk 4 WK273 at Farnborough in 1954

This is the rear view of the two-tier 3in rocket projectiles under the port wing of F Mk 4 WK273 at Farnborough in 1954. These are inert rounds, namely because they are painted black (the colour used for inert at that time, later it was blue) and they have no rocket motors, hence the lack of the weak link 'pigtails' at the back

This is a Fireflash test round in its handling trolley before being fitted under the wing of an F Mk 7 of the GWDS. The black and white paint eases tracking these via high-speed camera

Here you can see Fireflash missiles under the wings of F Mk 7 XF124

This shot of XF124 after firing one Fireflash does allow you to see the shape of the pylons used to carry these missiles

8.3 Weapons – Ventral Tank

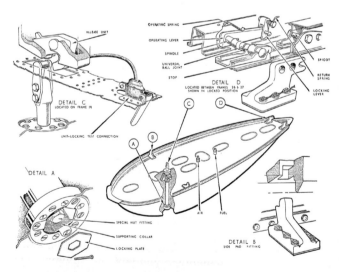

Here is the component diagram of the jettisonable fuel tank, this comes from the F Mks 1 and 2 manual, but it applies to all versions except the F Mk 7
(©Crown Copyright)

This is the 200 Imp. Gal. ventral tank seen underneath FR Mk 5 WK296 at Farnborough in 1956

This is an overall photo of the tank under FR Mk 5 WK277

9.1 Electrical Equipment – Radio

This is the main fuse box fitted in the mid-fuselage of F Mk 4 WK275
(©Jet Art Aviation Ltd)

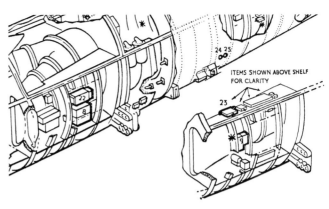

This extract from a location diagram shows where the radio equipment (marked '22' and '8') is in the fuselage *(©Crown Copyright)*

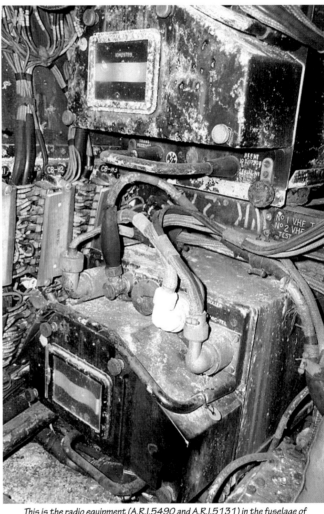

This is the radio equipment (A.R.I.5490 and A.R.I.5131) in the fuselage of F Mk 4 WK275. The top item is '22' in the previous diagram, whilst the lower one is '8' *(©Crown Copyright)*

9.2 Electrical Equipment – Camera

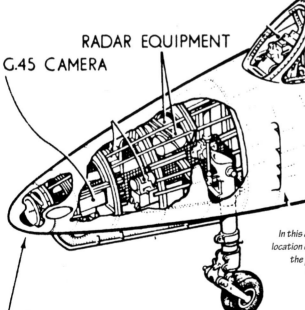

RADAR EQUIPMENT

G.45 CAMERA

NOSE CAP
AND RADOME

In this diagram you can see the location of the G.45 camera gun in the port side of the nose
(©Crown Copyright)

On the F Mks 2, 3 and 4, the camera gun port was on the port side of the nose, as seen in this front view of F Mk 4 WK273

Here is a close-up of the camera gun port in the nose of F Mk 4 WK275 during restoration (©Jet Art Aviation Ltd)

This is the G.45 camera gun, made by Williamson (©via Internet)

With the FR Mk 5 a camera was located in the nose, with the main cameras in either side and further back. This photo shows the camera port in the nose cap of FR Mk 5 WK281

Here you can see the oblique camera port in the port side of the nose in FR Mk 5 WK277

PRE-LENS FILTER HOLDER

This is the strip-aperture F.95 camera fitted obliquely on either side of the nose of the FR Mk 5. It could use a 4in or 12in lens

Here is the camera port in the starboard side of the nose of FR Mk 5 WK290

10.1 Miscellaneous Equipment

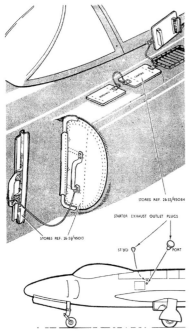

Intake blanking plates and plugs, seen here in the diagram from the F Mk 4 manual (©Crown Copyright)

Here is a front view of the access ladder fitted to the F Mk 7 cockpit section with the BDAC, this style of ladder was used for all variants

The access ladder on the BDAC F Mk 7, this time viewed from the rear

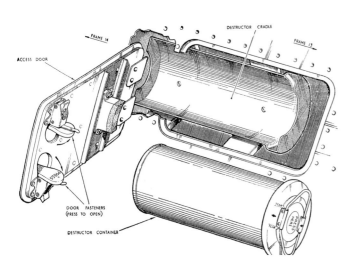

This is the aircraft destructor charge, which is situated on the starboard fuselage side between frames 13 and 14 (©Crown Copyright)

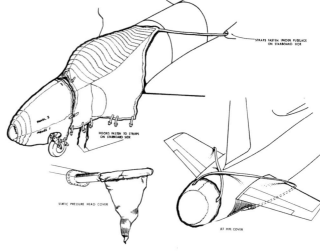

This diagram shows the aircraft covers for the F Mk 4, but they apply to the F Mks 1 to 3, plus in slightly revised forms to take account of the revised nose, the FR Mk 5 and F Mk 7 (©Crown Copyright)

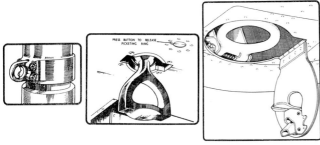

This diagram shows the picketing for the F Mk 4, but it applies to all variants (©Crown Copyright)

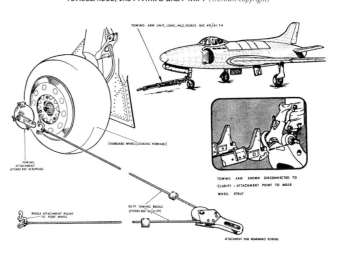

This is how the Swift was towed, via a towing arm to the nose wheel and a towing bridle to each main wheel hub (©Crown Copyright)

The Type 535 (VV119) seen from the port side with the dummy cannon fairings fitted for the 1950 Farnborough event. The roundels are Type D as is the fin flash, but it is higher up the fin than the Type 510 had it, plus you can see that the fuselage prototype 'P' once again has a dotted outer ring to it. The large warning stencil, on a red block, on the intake was only seen for a short time on this machine

Section 2

Camouflage & Markings

The Swift is a sufficiently modern type for colour photos to exist of it in service, plus all the painting regulations that effect its service career also still exist, so this allows us to be pretty certain about what colours and markings were applied throughout the type's service career. This whole subject of camouflage and markings is massive however, you can write volumes and many have, so we will try and keep it concise. Just remember, nothing is an absolute when it comes to camouflage and markings.

The Type 510 (VV106) seen with the blunt nose. The Type C1 fuselage roundel and fin flash are evident and in the original images you can make out that the surround for the prototype 'P' is in fact a dotted line, not a continual one. Note also the anti-creep marks painted across the hub/tyres of the tailwheel

Prototypes

In its initial form the Type 510 (VV106) looks to be painted aluminium overall, as the term 'High Speed Silver' was not adopted until four years later (in January 1953). The roundels were Type D applied above and below the wings and either side of the fuselage. These all look to be 24in diameter and the position of those under the wings was determined by the serial number, which was applied in 48in high black characters, read from the leading edge looking aft on the starboard side and from the trailing edge looking forward on the port. The serial was also applied in 8in high black characters on

VV106 on HMS Illustrious during deck trials in November 1950, the roundels under the wing can be seen on the original and are Type D, so we presume the fuselage ones are as well. The fin flash has also changed, both in style and position

Here is the Type 510 (VV106) at Farnborough in September 1949, with the pointed nose cap. The fuselage roundel and fin flash are Type D and you can make out the various stencils applied around the cockpit area

This angle of VV119 in flight is useful as it confirms the application of the Type D roundels above the wings, plus you can see the dotted circle to the 'P' and the usual style of stencilling on the fuselage

This shot of VV119 as it banks away from the camera is useful because it confirms the Type D roundels under the wings, their position and the fact that the serial number is applied in a stencil style character, with gaps in the top of the '9' being the most obvious (©Vickers)

A nice official shot of the port side of the first pre-production Swift, Type 541 WJ960, in which you can see the standard application of the Type D roundels and fin flash, plus the serial nearly underneath the tailplanes. The stencils on the nose are very much like VV119 (©Ministry of Supply)

either side of the rear fuselage, with the last three digits effectively under the tailplane trailing edge at its root. The fin flash was Type D and was not square, so I suspect this was 24in wide by 27in high. It was positioned with the aft lower corner at the rudder hinge line and ran along the fairing on top of the fuselage, which resulted in the upper front section being truncated by the fin leading edge. The prototype P marking was applied between the fuselage roundel and serial number and it is much larger than the former, so probably 52in. Stencils can clearly be seen on the airframe, with the likes of the 'Sling' markings being applied in small black characters, whilst the '24 Volt' warning on the port side of the nose is in yellow and uses a very stylised block font type. The ejection seat warning triangle is the early style, without the outer white/red edge and it is applied on either side of the nose, just below the cockpit within the boundary of the intake; it is flanked on either side by the word 'Danger' in red. The other marking on either side of the nose

In this shot of WJ960 you can clearly see the location of the serial numbers under the wings, plus the location and size of the roundels (©C.E. Brown)

comprises three lines of text, all in red, with the upper one in characters twice as large stating 'Danger' and below this in smaller characters are two lines stating 'Keep well away from intakes' on the top line, then 'when engine is running' below and these are applied in capital letters throughout. The stencil just above the intake on either side is in black and it is a combination of letters

and numbers relating to a DTD specification for the fuel type/capacity. There is another stencil just forward of the canopy on the starboard side only, but period images are not sufficiently clear to see exactly what it says; I suspect this is a 'chop here in case of emergency' marking because it includes a red arrow pointing back to the canopy surround. Underneath, the only stencils I

This in-flight image of the second pre-production Swift WJ965 nicely shows the size and location of the Type D roundels and fin flash. The vertical fin has the extension in front of it, which is a mix of metal tones and some sections that are painted/primed (©Ministry of Supply)

Swift F Mk 1s WK205, WK206, WK211 and WK212 on their way from South Marston to AFDS West Raynham in February 1954. They all display the initial overall aluminium scheme of the series with Type D markings, the serial just under the tailplane and the nose cone painted blue (©Vickers)

can see are 'No step' markings on the flaps, ailerons, elevators and tailplanes, the latter two applied at the mind point, whilst the former two are close together (outboard on the flaps and inboard on the ailerons). There also looks to be a stencil outboard of each roundel, so these may be 'Sling' markings.

The Type 510 was modified in 1950 with a rounded nose that no longer contained a pitot, which was initially moved to the top of the vertical fin, but was later supplemented by a second one at the port wing tip. Here the confusion really starts, as there are images of this machine doing deck landings on HMS Illustrious on the 17th November 1950 that clearly show the aircraft still in aluminium and with almost identical markings to its original form, but the fin flash is Type D, 24in wide by 27in high and positioned parallel with the rudder hinge line, thus sloping backwards on the fin. Sadly we have found no photos at this stage that confirm the fuselage roundel type, nor if the prototype marking

As WJ965 banks away from the camera, you can see the smaller Type D roundels out by the tips plus the size/location/orientation of the serial numbers under each wing; these are solid characters this time, not the stencil style seen on VV119 (©Ministry of Supply)

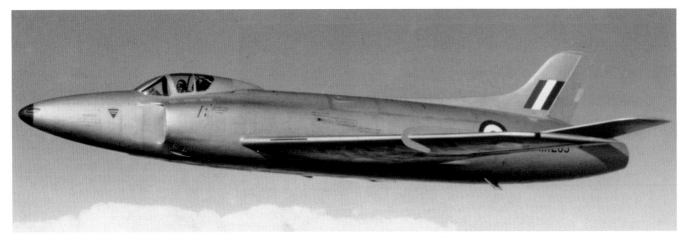

A lovely colour shot of WK205 en-route to West Raynham in February 1954, you can see the overall scheme is paint not bare metal, and the nose cap is a dark blue, that is not quite as dark as the Oxford Blue of the roundels (©Vickers)

A good shot of F Mk 1 WK206 with No.56 Squadron, sporting the red/white checks flanking the fuselage roundel that was used by the squadron. The aft-most squares almost touch the serial number, whilst those alongside the roundel are longer on their top edge due to the arc of the roundel

This shot of an unknown F Mk 1 is included to show how the maintenance serial numbers were applied in place of the serial number once the airframe was no longer active. The No.56 Squadron checks are in evidence, and the maintenance code is applied back-to-front, as it should be '7314M', but this is quote common on Swifts relegated to ground use

The mis-applied maintenance serial was common as already stated, and confirmed here by this view of F Mk 3 7341M marked as 'M7341' and used by No.8 SofTT Weeton in 1957. The application of the trainer yellow bands around fuselage and wings is unique though, as the type was never marked as such operationally (©R.J. Caruana)

WK247 was the first of 25 F Mk 3s delivered and in this shot you can see the green and grey camouflage on the upper surfaces, as well as the size/location of the Type D roundels on the wings (©British Official)

one with 'Ejection Seat' in the middle of the triangle and 'Danger' applied in red parallel to each side. The warning stencils for the intakes remained, but the '24 Volt' stencil was gone and replaced by a much larger stencil on four lines contained within the oblong access panel at this point (it refers to the compass amongst other things).

Production

F Mk 1

The first production F Mk 1s were aluminium overall with Type D roundels on the fuselage and wings, plus a similar type fin flash. This latter item was set parallel to the rudder hinge line, so it slopes backwards on either side of the vertical fin. The serial was applied in 8in high black characters either side of the rear fuselage, with nearly all of it underneath the tailplanes. The location of this is not consistent on images from the period, showing that some machines had the whole serial number positioned so that the forward-most character on either side was no further forward that the tailplane leading edge/root junction point, while others have the front character clear of this point, thus projecting slightly further forward on the fuselage side. The serial was repeated in black characters under each wing, with those under the starboard side read from the leading edge looking aft, and those under the port from the trailing edge looking forward. Michael J.F. Bowyer noted that in 1955 he saw F Mk 1s of No.56 Squadron, one of which (WK211) had these serial numbers applied in the same way under both wings, read from the trailing edge looking forward!

was applied. What is odd is that there is another well-known and very clear image of this machine in flight that shows it with the same wing roundels etc., but with the fin flash as the older Type C1, applied vertically and thus truncated by the leading edge of the fin (it is positioned well forward on the fin) plus it also has the older style C1 roundel on each side of the fuselage? The prototype marking is aft of the roundel and slightly larger, plus the outer ring is a dotted line, not a continual one. At this stage the airframe does not have the extra pitot on the port wing tip, nor does it have the angle of attack probe (like an Attacker) above the nose cone that you can see fitted during the deck trials. We have to therefore assume that this scheme in fact pre-dates that applied to it by the time of the decking landing trials? There is a thought that this machine received a new Attacker fuselage straight off the production line, which would thus have had the older style roundel and fin flash, but that is not confirmed.

The second prototype was initially built as a Type 528 and flew as such in March 1950, however we have found no images of this machine in this configuration (it only flew in this configuration for less than three months), but assume it also would have been aluminium with the same style of markings seen on the later version of VV106? It was extensively modified three months later to become the Type 535 and emerged in bare metal with the same style Type D roundels and fin flash seen on VV106, although the latter was applied parallel to the rudder hinge line and thus sloped backwards. The serial number was

again applied under each wing, in the same style/size/location and the roundels were outboard of this as a result. The revised wing meant that the fuselage roundel was applied above the centreline and over the rearmost section of the wing root fairing (the serial number remained on the centreline). Stencilling looks to be pretty much as the initial Type 510, although there are no 'Sling' markings on the mid and aft fuselage. The ejection seat triangle was the revised

As F Mk 3 WK247 banks away you can see the demarcation between upper and lower colours, plus the style/ location of the roundels under the wings and the orientation/location/style of the serial numbers under each wing. You can also make out that the stencils on the camouflaged areas are light (yellow), whilst those on the underside are dark (black). The image confirms that the wrap-around of the upper surface camouflage seen on the later FR Mk 5 was not done with the F Mk 3 (©British Official)

F Mk 1 WK198 acted as the prototype for the F Mk 4 series, but it also set a World Speed Record and is seen here prior to that event in its overall 'pale blue' scheme. Note that the wing fences were removed for the record attempt (©Air Ministry)

the upper surfaces and aluminium underneath. The national insignia remained as with the F Mk 1 and the red/white checks either side of the fuselage roundel were also retained, along with these checks on the wing tips. The individual aircraft number either side of the vertical fin was applied in red instead of black and to offer more contrast it was thinly (1/2in) outlined in white. The ejection seat triangles remained the same, but the dark camouflage meant that the lettering was no longer clear (thus showing through the aluminium underneath), but white. The marking stencil ahead of the triangle on the port side of the nose was no longer just red text, it was now white text applied to a red oblong, again to gain contrast with the camouflage underneath.

F Mk 3
See the notes at the start of the F Mk 4 section for comments relating to WK195, the prototype F Mk 3. This machine was also seen in the overall aluminium scheme, with the same style, size and location of markings seen on the F Mk 1. Only 25 F Mk 3s were built and most of these were delivered by road to be used as instructional airframes and none of them served with operational units. These machines were supplied from the manufacturer in the same basic camouflage scheme seen on the F Mk 2s and had the same national insignia etc., but they never had individual code letters, because they were never issued to units.

F Mk 4
Only eight Mk 4s were built and the prototype, WK198, was seen in an overall 'light blue' scheme, so visions of the prototype Spitfire come to mind. In fact WK195 the F Mk 3 prototype was also in this scheme and both were seen together at the SBAC event at Farnborough in 1953. Colour photos exist in the Peter R. Arnold collection, although it is difficult to determine the exact shade, because it certainly looks a lot darker than most profiles depict it, plus also a bit greener? The nose cap of WK198 was definitely red, not dark blue or black as some depict

The nose cap was painted either black, red or blue, probably using the new 'bright' (BS-standard) colours for the latter two as used in the Type D markings. The ejection seat warning triangle was applied on either side of the nose, forward of a line down from the front edge of the windscreen.

No.56 Squadron machines retained the above-mentioned overall markings, but also had red and white checks (6 1/2in) applied either side of the fuselage roundels (the top and base line of those checks adjacent to the roundel were 8 1/2in). These blocks were made up of two rows and four checks, either side of the roundel. The squadron also

repeated this marking on the extreme tips of the wings, both above and below (wrapping round). An individual aircraft letter was usually applied above the fin flash on either side in black, with the vertical axis of this character parallel to the rudder hinge. The orientation of the letter and the slope meant that those on the starboard side sloped back, whilst those on the port sloped forward.

F Mk 2
By the time the F Mk 2 was operated by No.56 Squadron it had a tactical camouflage scheme applied, this being a disruptive pattern of Dark Green and Dark Sea Grey on

Swift FR Mk 5s of No.2 Squadron line up with XD916 being the nearest. You can see the triangles on the horizontal bars are white with this machine, plus you can also make out the darker dielectric panel on the top/front of the vertical fin. All the warning stencils seem to be in yellow, whilst information ones are black (©Air Ministry)

No F Mk 4 was used operationally, but this image of WK273 at Farnborough shows the overall scheme and markings applied to the type by the factory (©Ministry of Supply)

and all the other markings were standard RAF Type D, with the serial in black under the tailplanes and each wing. All the other F Mk 4s would have been completed in the same Dark Sea Grey/Dark Green over aluminium, with the same Type D roundels and fin flash as per the F Mks 2 and 3.

FR Mk 5

The aerodynamic prototype for the FR Mk 5 was WK200 and this was converted from a F Mk 1. It was therefore in the overall aluminium scheme of the F Mk 1, with the same Type D roundels and fin flash, although this latter item was shorter than those seen on the later variants.

When the FR Mk 5 went into service use it was in the Dark Sea Grey and Dark Green scheme used on previous versions, but the undersides were in PRU Blue to better fit in with the photo-reconnaissance role of the type. The upper camouflage wrapped around the leading edge of both the wings and tailplanes. The roundels remained Type D, as was the fin flash, and all the stencils were now applied in yellow on the camouflage. Usually in squadron service each aircraft would have an individual identifying letter and this was normally applied above the fin flash on either side of the vertical fin. This letter can be seen applied either in a normal (vertical) format, or sloping parallel with the rudder hinge line. These letters could be yellow or white and it would seem that those of No.2 Squadron had the letter applied in a larger format white character and this was positioned at the top of the vertical fin, some distance above the top of the fin flash.

Unit colours were applied in horizontal bars either side of the fuselage roundel. For No.79 Squadron this was a red arrowhead, which pointed to the front of the aircraft on both side of the fuselage. No.2 Squadron had a black bar with a white triangle in the middle. In later life the FR Mk 5 had the PRU Blue undersides removed and this area was then painted High Speed Silver (as aluminium was now called) overall, with the usual application of the serial numbers in black characters as per the F Mks 2, 3 and 4.

This is a well-known image claiming to show a formation of No.2 Squadron FR Mk 5s, however very close examination of the image seems to indicate that this in in fact a montage, using one aircraft image stacked one on top of the other. Only the bottom aircraft has serial numbers, the rest have had them removed, plus the pilot in each one is exactly the same! The multiple exposures have also lead to a gradual darkening of the aircraft as they stack up, which is contrary, as they would all receive similar light levels, but this does mean that the triangles on the vertical bars either side of the roundel are a mix of the correct white and a darker shade many claim are red. If you are still not convinced, check out the tip of the vertical fin on the second from the top, where it goes over the underside of the aircraft above/behind it, there is a very thin faint white outline caused by the negative overlays. Our assessment of this may not be correct, but we are pretty sure and the only way to disprove it will be when someone comes up with the original negative…, over to you (©Air Ministry/MOD)

Swift FR Mk 5s of No. 79 Squadron format with Hunters from Nos. 14 (lower) and 25 (upper) Squadrons. The colour image allows you to determine that the nearest machine has PRU Blue undersides, whilst the furthest one is still aluminium (High Speed Silver by this date) underneath (©Air Ministry/MOD)

Swift F Mk 7 XF124 in the standard green/grey over aluminium scheme of the series. Note the black tip to the nose and the last three of the serial number repeated in black on the nose wheel door

(©Air Ministry/MOD)

Swift F Mk 7 XF114 was used for runway trials and is seen here in the 1960s having completed these, but still in its overall black scheme, with the calibration marks added in white on the dorsal spine

(©A.W. Hall†)

Swift FR Mk 5 XD962 was the personal aircraft of Sqn Ldr C.S. MacDonald from No. 2 Squadron and you can see his name was applied in yellow characters on a black bar on either side of the nose, with his rank pennant ahead of it

PR Mk 6

Only one PR Mk 6 was completed, it never reached squadron use and ended up at Halton, where it was never unpacked and ended up being scrapped. It is most likely that it was never painted, or if it was, it was in the Dark Sea Grey/Dark Green/PRU Blue scheme of the FR Mk 5. It would be good to think of the type in service, as a Medium Sea Grey over PRU Blue would have looked good!

F Mk 7

Nearly all of the F Mk 7s were used for guided weapons development with the GWDS and these had the same scheme applied to the F Mks 2, 3 and 4 plus the later FR Mk 5s, namely Dark Sea Grey/Dark Green over High Speed Silver. The roundels and fin flash were Type D and the serial was applied in 8in black characters in the usual place on either side of the rear fuselage. The last three of the serial were also applied on the nose undercarriage door, again in 8in high black characters. The nose cap was normally black, with the ring just behind this in bare aluminium.

One of the most 'colourful' Swifts is XF114, which although initially in the above scheme, was later painted black overall, which had a satin sheen to it. Type D roundels and fin flash remained, but the serial on the rear fuselage was now in white to contrast. No images exist to confirm that the underside serials were applied, or if these

Swift FR Mk 5 XD907 in vertical climb, showing off nicely its PRU Blue undersides, including a lot of wear and tear to paint in this area, plus the way the upper camouflage wraps around the leading edge of both wings and tailplanes. This machine is in the two-cannon configuration, with only the inboard cannon ports open (©Air Ministry)

were also in white, but we presume they were? All stencils are very visible and colour images confirm these were all in white, while the ejection seat warning triangle was red with white lettering. Applied on either side

of the forward nose was a cartoon depicting Donald Duck skidding along and this related to the aquaplaning trials the type was undertaking. Later calibration white bars were applied to the upper fuselage, these forming a cross with a third bar applied horizontally through the centre of the cross (the cross was orientated as an 'X' with the central bar's tips pointing to each wing tip), there also looks to have been another half bar applied to the rear of the cross, just touching the base of the vertical fin extension. When this machine concluded the trials and ended up at the Flint Technical College it initially retained these markings, but the black soon deteriorated and so it was repainted. Initially this new scheme was pale cream (some state white, but colour photos show it to be off-white or cream) with the upper 1/4 of the fuselage encompassing the entire vertical fin/rudder in red. The demarcation was not level and it did not include the canopy surround, which was pale cream, then the demarcation curved quickly together ahead of the windscreen, so that 3/4 of the nose was all pale cream. The fin flash looks to have a very thin outline in pale cream? A stylised rearing Welsh dragon looking more like a Griffon was applied on either side of the nose, just forward of the intakes. It is difficult to determine if the other scheme applied to this machine was applied before or after the above mentioned one, but at it retained the Dragon and now had a stylised

In this shot of F MK 7 XF124 as it banks away, you can see the extended wing tips, and the way the upper camouflage wraps around the leading edge of the wings and tailplanes (©Ministry of Supply/MOD)

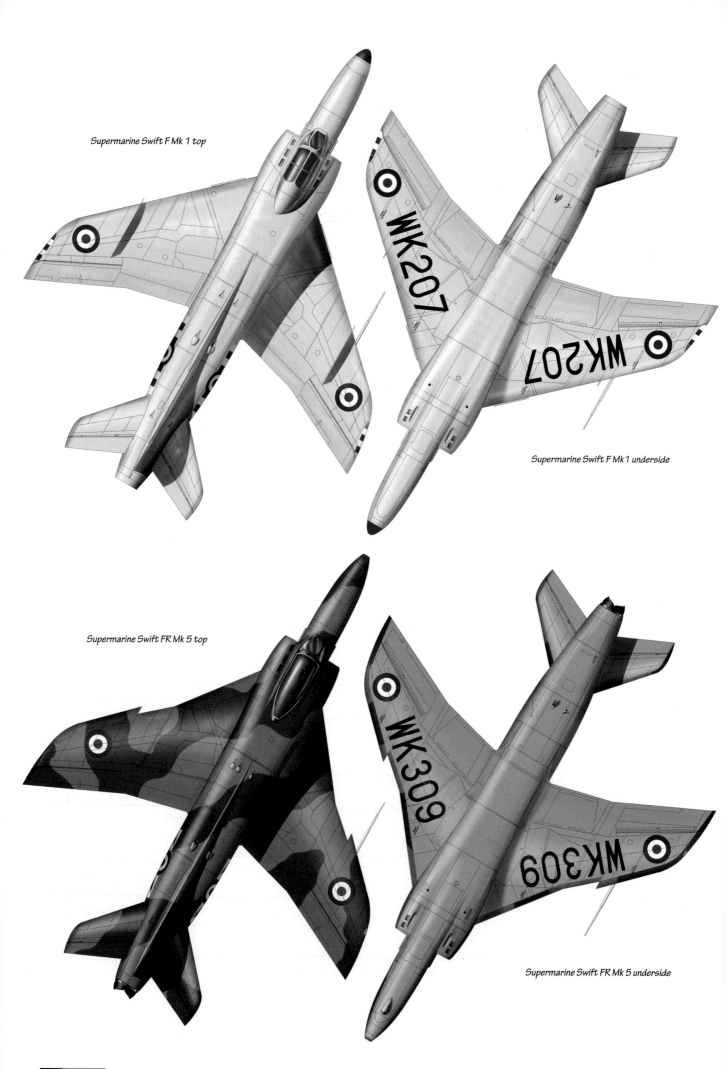

Supermarine Swift F Mk 1 top

Supermarine Swift F Mk 1 underside

Supermarine Swift FR Mk 5 top

Supermarine Swift FR Mk 5 underside

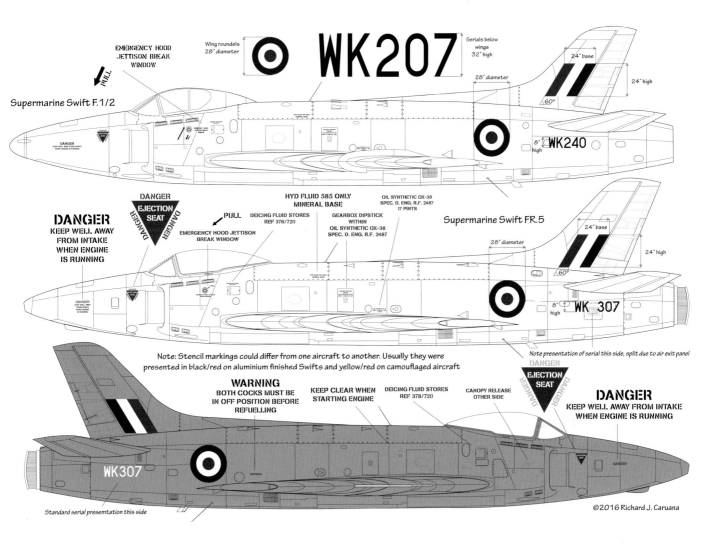

Supermarine Swift F.1/2

EMERGENCY HOOD
JETTISON BREAK
WINDOW
PULL

Wing roundels
28" diameter

WK207

Serials below
wings
32" high

24" base

28" diameter

24" high

60°

WK240

8" high

DANGER
EJECTION
SEAT
DANGER

DANGER
KEEP WELL AWAY
FROM INTAKE
WHEN ENGINE
IS RUNNING

PULL

EMERGENCY HOOD JETTISON
BREAK WINDOW

HYD FLUID 585 ONLY
MINERAL BASE

DEICING FLUID STORES
REF 378/720

GEARBOX DIPSTICK
WITHIN
OIL SYNTHETIC OX-38
SPEC. D. ENG. R.F. 2487

OIL SYNTHETIC OX-38
SPEC. D. ENG. R.F. 2487
17 PINTS

Supermarine Swift FR.5

24" base

28" diameter

24" high

60°

WK 307

8" high

DANGER
KEEP WELL
FROM INTAKE
WHEN ENGINE
IS RUNNING

Note: Stencil markings could differ from one aircraft to another. Usually they were
presented in black/red on aluminium finished Swifts and yellow/red on camouflaged aircraft

Note presentation of serial this side, split due to air exit panel

WARNING
BOTH COCKS MUST BE
IN OFF POSITION BEFORE
REFUELLING

KEEP CLEAR WHEN
STARTING ENGINE

DEICING FLUID STORES
REF 378/720

CANOPY RELEASE
OTHER SIDE

DANGER
EJECTION
SEAT
DANGER

DANGER
KEEP WELL AWAY FROM INTAKE
WHEN ENGINE IS RUNNING

WK307

DANGER

Standard serial presemtation this side

©2016 Richard J. Caruana

'Swift' text applied to the front of the nose on the port side only. The overall scheme was now very, very faded and you can just make out red on the starboard side of the vertical fin/rudder, but the port side is completely stripped. All of the markings were extremely faded and the overall condition of the airframe was very poor, after years stationary outside in all weathers.

Colour Specifications

- Aluminium (for metal): Cellulose DTD 63, Synthetic DTD 260
- Aluminium pigmented lightweight lacquer: Cellulose DTD 766
- Dark Green BS381C-641
- Dark Sea Grey BS381C-638 Cellulose DTD 751-754, Synthetic DTD 314
- PRU Blue BS381C-636 Cellulose DTD 751-754, Synthetic DTD 314
- Night BS381C-642
- Bright Red BS 381C-538
- White: There is no BS 381C match for this colour, nor was it included in the MofS colour range
- Bright Blue BS381C-110
- Yellow BS 381C - There is no BS 381C match for this colour, but MofS Aircraft Finish No.405 in the mid-1950s was close enough to make its inclusion in BS 381C pointless

Here is a close-up of the skidding Donald Duck cartoon applied to either side of the nose of XF114

We would also recommend the following titles for those wishing to read more on the subject of post-war RAF camouflage and markings:

- Fighting Colours: RAF Fighter Camouflage and Markings 1937-1969 by M.J.F. Bowyer (ISBN: 85059 041 8 Patrick Stephens Ltd 1969)

- RAF Fighters 1945-1950 UK Based, Camouflage & Marking No.1 by Paul Lucas (Guidelines Publications Ltd)

Supermarine Swift F Mk 1, WK208 (later coded 'A'), No.56 Squadron, Waterbeach, February 1954
Aluminium overall with standard national markings; fuselage roundel flanked by red/white checks, repeated on wing tips. Black serial, repeated below wings; black nose cone

Supermarine Swift F Mk 1, WK207/N, No.56 Squadron, Waterbeach, February 1954
Aluminium overall with standard national markings. Fuselage roundels flanked by red/white checks, repeated on wing tips. 'N' in red outlined in white, on fin; serial in black, repeated below wings

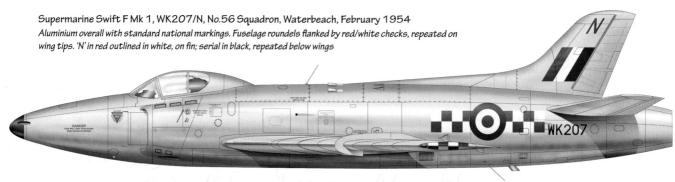

Supermarine Swift F Mk 1, M7312 (ex-WK205/G of No.56 Squadron),
No.8 School of Technical Training, Weeton, September 1957
Aluminium overall with standard national markings, Fuselage roundels flanked by red/white checks, repeated on wingtips. 'G' in red, outlined in white, on fin; serial in black

Supermarine Swift F Mk 2, WK240/E, No.56 Squadron
Dark Sea Grey (BS.81C-638) and Dark Green (BS.381C-641) upper surfaces with Aluminium undersides. Standard national markings. Black serial, repeated below the wings. Red 'E' on fin outlined in white. Red/white checks flanking fuselage roundels, repeated on wingtips

Supermarine Swift F Mk 2, WK242/P, of No.56 Squadron operating from Waterbeach
Dark Sea Grey (BS.81C-638) and Dark Green (BS.381C-641) upper surfaces with Aluminium undersides. Standard national markings. Black serial, repeated below the wings. Red 'P' on fin outlined in white. Red/white checks flanking fuselage roundels, repeated on wingtips. It joined the unit on 10th September 1954 and was retired after barely six months of service

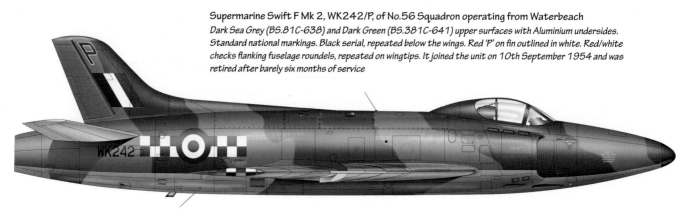

A

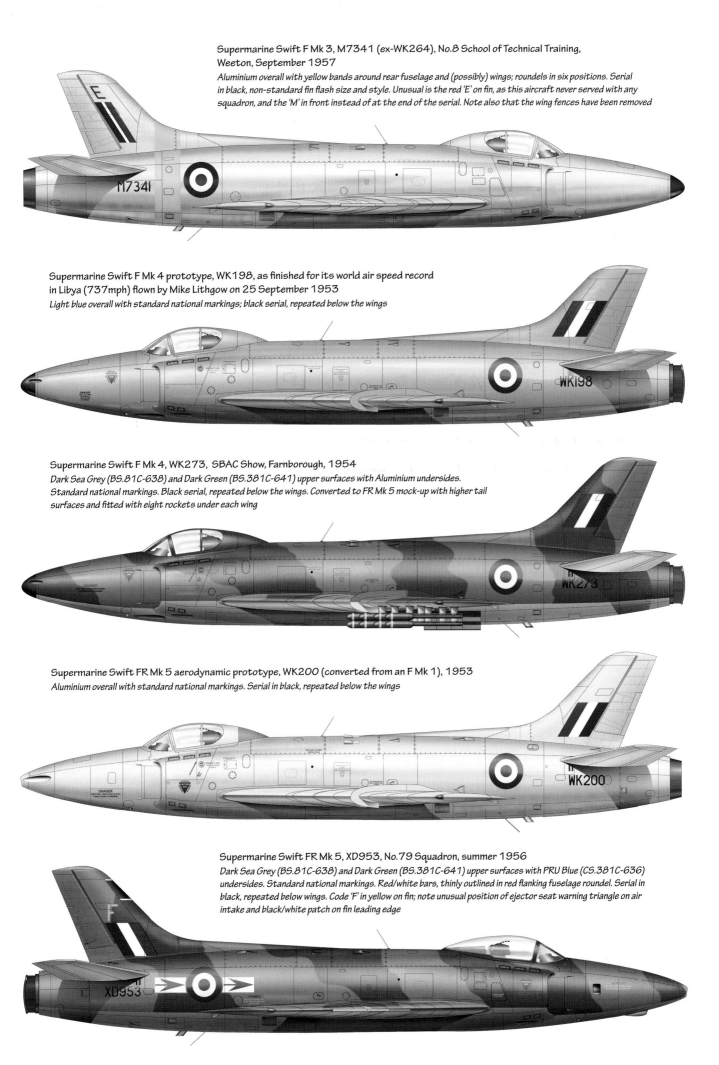

Supermarine Swift F Mk 3, M7341 (ex-WK264), No.8 School of Technical Training,
Weeton, September 1957
*Aluminium overall with yellow bands around rear fuselage and (possibly) wings; roundels in six positions. Serial
in black, non-standard fin flash size and style. Unusual is the red 'E' on fin, as this aircraft never served with any
squadron, and the 'M' in front instead of at the end of the serial. Note also that the wing fences have been removed*

Supermarine Swift F Mk 4 prototype, WK198, as finished for its world air speed record
in Libya (737mph) flown by Mike Lithgow on 25 September 1953
Light blue overall with standard national markings; black serial, repeated below the wings

Supermarine Swift F Mk 4, WK273, SBAC Show, Farnborough, 1954
*Dark Sea Grey (BS.81C-638) and Dark Green (BS.381C-641) upper surfaces with Aluminium undersides.
Standard national markings. Black serial, repeated below the wings. Converted to FR Mk 5 mock-up with higher tail
surfaces and fitted with eight rockets under each wing*

Supermarine Swift FR Mk 5 aerodynamic prototype, WK200 (converted from an F Mk 1), 1953
Aluminium overall with standard national markings. Serial in black, repeated below the wings

Supermarine Swift FR Mk 5, XD953, No.79 Squadron, summer 1956
*Dark Sea Grey (BS.81C-638) and Dark Green (BS.381C-641) upper surfaces with PRU Blue (CS.381C-636)
undersides. Standard national markings. Red/white bars, thinly outlined in red flanking fuselage roundel. Serial in
black, repeated below wings. Code 'F' in yellow on fin; note unusual position of ejector seat warning triangle on air
intake and black/white patch on fin leading edge*

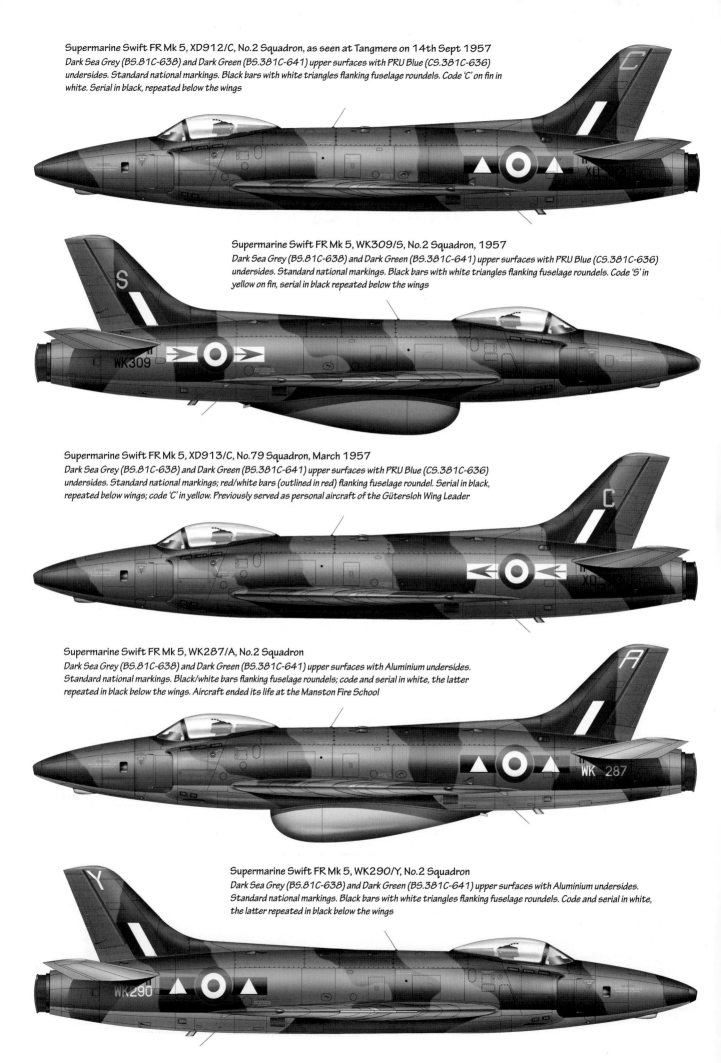

Supermarine Swift FR Mk 5, XD912/C, No.2 Squadron, as seen at Tangmere on 14th Sept 1957
Dark Sea Grey (BS.81C-638) and Dark Green (BS.381C-641) upper surfaces with PRU Blue (CS.381C-636) undersides. Standard national markings. Black bars with white triangles flanking fuselage roundels. Code 'C' on fin in white. Serial in black, repeated below the wings

Supermarine Swift FR Mk 5, WK309/S, No.2 Squadron, 1957
Dark Sea Grey (BS.81C-638) and Dark Green (BS.381C-641) upper surfaces with PRU Blue (CS.381C-636) undersides. Standard national markings. Black bars with white triangles flanking fuselage roundels. Code 'S' in yellow on fin, serial in black repeated below the wings

Supermarine Swift FR Mk 5, XD913/C, No.79 Squadron, March 1957
Dark Sea Grey (BS.81C-638) and Dark Green (BS.381C-641) upper surfaces with PRU Blue (CS.381C-636) undersides. Standard national markings; red/white bars (outlined in red) flanking fuselage roundel. Serial in black, repeated below wings; code 'C' in yellow. Previously served as personal aircraft of the Gütersloh Wing Leader

Supermarine Swift FR Mk 5, WK287/A, No.2 Squadron
Dark Sea Grey (BS.81C-638) and Dark Green (BS.381C-641) upper surfaces with Aluminium undersides. Standard national markings. Black/white bars flanking fuselage roundels; code and serial in white, the latter repeated in black below the wings. Aircraft ended its life at the Manston Fire School

Supermarine Swift FR Mk 5, WK290/Y, No.2 Squadron
Dark Sea Grey (BS.81C-638) and Dark Green (BS.381C-641) upper surfaces with Aluminium undersides. Standard national markings. Black bars with white triangles flanking fuselage roundels. Code and serial in white, the latter repeated in black below the wings

C

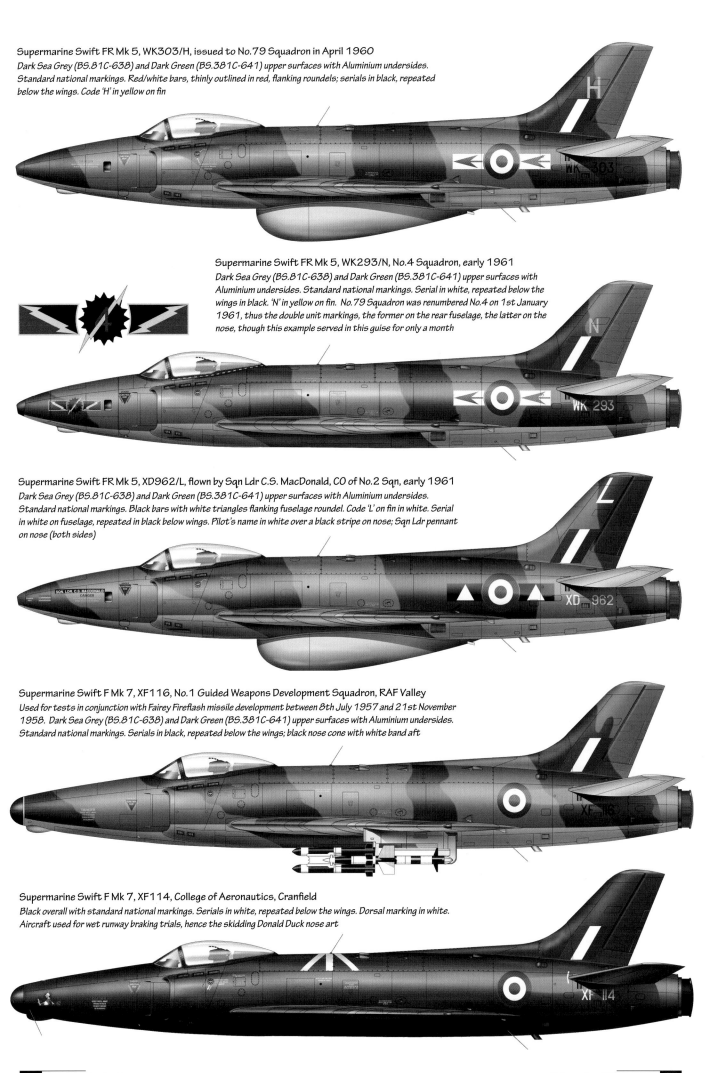

Supermarine Swift FR Mk 5, WK303/H, issued to No.79 Squadron in April 1960
Dark Sea Grey (BS.81C-638) and Dark Green (BS.381C-641) upper surfaces with Aluminium undersides.
Standard national markings. Red/white bars, thinly outlined in red, flanking roundels; serials in black, repeated
below the wings. Code 'H' in yellow on fin

Supermarine Swift FR Mk 5, WK293/N, No.4 Squadron, early 1961
Dark Sea Grey (BS.81C-638) and Dark Green (BS.381C-641) upper surfaces with
Aluminium undersides. Standard national markings. Serial in white, repeated below the
wings in black. 'N' in yellow on fin. No.79 Squadron was renumbered No.4 on 1st January
1961, thus the double unit markings, the former on the rear fuselage, the latter on the
nose, though this example served in this guise for only a month

Supermarine Swift FR Mk 5, XD962/L, flown by Sqn Ldr C.S. MacDonald, CO of No.2 Sqn, early 1961
Dark Sea Grey (BS.81C-638) and Dark Green (BS.381C-641) upper surfaces with Aluminium undersides.
Standard national markings. Black bars with white triangles flanking fuselage roundel. Code 'L' on fin in white. Serial
in white on fuselage, repeated in black below wings. Pilot's name in white over a black stripe on nose; Sqn Ldr pennant
on nose (both sides)

Supermarine Swift F Mk 7, XF116, No.1 Guided Weapons Development Squadron, RAF Valley
Used for tests in conjunction with Fairey Fireflash missile development between 8th July 1957 and 21st November
1958. Dark Sea Grey (BS.81C-638) and Dark Green (BS.381C-641) upper surfaces with Aluminium undersides.
Standard national markings. Serials in black, repeated below the wings; black nose cone with white band aft

Supermarine Swift F Mk 7, XF114, College of Aeronautics, Cranfield
Black overall with standard national markings. Serials in white, repeated below the wings. Dorsal marking in white.
Aircraft used for wet runway braking trials, hence the skidding Donald Duck nose art

Building a FR Mk 5

Built by Richard A. Franks

Kit box

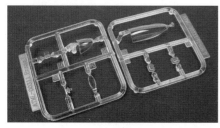

Clear parts

Technical Specifications
Manufacturer: Airfix, United Kingdom
Scale: 1/72nd
Kit No.: A04003
Materials: Injection-moulded plastic
Parts Count:
Decal Options: 2
UK Price: £16.99
Price is correct at time of going to press

Few kits have ever been offered of the Swift, the old Hawk one in 1/72nd being the one most will know, but there have been limited-run injection moulded plastic (Xtrakits), vac-formed plastic (Formaplane & Rareplanes) and resin (Czechmaster and Magna Models) kits in 1/72nd scale plus the well-known vac-formed example from Falcon. Today however we have a brand new, modern quality, main-stream, injection moulded plastic kit of the Swift in 1/72nd from Airfix, so we thought we would include a quick build of it.

Construction

This starts with the seat and I opted for the one with belts and just painted these. The tub builds up well, but leave off the GGS (F07) until final assembly. Now at stage 5 I found that if you add the nose wheel section to the built cockpit tub it is too long? Having test-fitted this I was able to correct it by trimming the back of the well until both sub-assembles lined up in the fuselage halves. The exhaust pipe in stage 7 was actually sprayed with Alclad 2 Jet Exhaust instead of the prescribed aluminium. When you do the intake splitter plates in stages 8 and 10, pre-paint D12 and D13 white as the instructions state, but then pre-paint the front sections (C06 and C07) in Dark Sea Grey and Dark Green respectively as this will help you later in the main painting stage. The side glazings in the nose fitted OK, remember to pre-spray the whole of the cockpit and nose area black before doing this, though, and that includes the holes for these glazed panels, as it will add depth and stop you having bare (grey) plastic visible. The front camera port (E05) was fiddly to

install, but it lined up eventually. The intake trunking in stage 16 builds up well and it's best to paint it as the grey plastic will be very visible inside otherwise. 2g of nose weight is required, but I did not have my natty new mini scales at this time, so I was worried I had not added enough due to the very limited space (made worse by the clear camera ports on either side), so I also superglued a weight behind the cockpit bulkhead, in between the intakes. Don't forget to open up the holes in the lower wing half in stage 19 for the ventral fuel tank, although you don't have to add this until the end. With the tailplanes, rudder and ailerons all installed, it was now time for some paint.

Colour Options

There are two schemes in the kit:
- WK281, flown by Flt Lt N. Warpole, No.79 Squadron, RAF Gütersloh, Germany, April 1956
- XD972, No.II (AC) Squadron, RAF Jever, Germany, 1956

I opted for the second option because I have never been a fan of the PRU Blue undersides. The basic 'aluminium' was an undercoat of Mr Surfacer Finishing 1500 (Black), then Alclad 2 White Aluminium at varying intensities. Once this had dried it was masked off and work on the upper colours could start (not forgetting, as I did initially, that the camo wraps around the front of the wing leading edges). As you always start with the lighter colour, this was Dark Sea Grey from the Gunze-Sangyo range. The initial application was a dense application along all the panel lines, then the remainder was 'filled in'. Once this had dried I could highlight certain panels with a lighter mix of the grey. Now the camouflage pattern was masked and the Dark Green applied, again from the Gunze-Sangyo range and again darker along the panel lines, then filling in the remainder. With all the masking off it was time to gloss down the whole airframe, so this was done with Johnson's Klear and left to dry for 48 hours to ensure it had cured fully.

Decals

These are well printed with perfect register and colour, although the images are satin and the carrier film can be seen around some of them. A full set of airframe stencils is included although as I found with the Vampire, the placement digram for these does, in numerous places, not relate to the panel lines on the model? This is something you just have to work round and see where is the most likely position for the stencil if the detail on the kit does not match that shown on the instructions. I found all the decals settled well with the use of Mr Mark Softener and I can't see any silvering, so a thumbs up.

Final Details

All of the parts that easily knock off had been prepared earlier, as the rest of the airframe was painted etc., so now these could be installed. The flaps go on no problem, although the attachment lugs don't seem to firmly meet anything, but they do hold? The oleo legs, wheels and undercarriage doors all assemble without problems. When you come to install them, though, you will soon discover that to fit them into the well, you have to initially install them at 90º to their final position, then once clear of the lip of the bay, you can rotate them back and they should sit snuggly into the recess in the bay roof. Next come the retraction arms (A08 and A09), what a nightmare, there are no real firm attachments and as the upper edge attaches to the oleo on the outer side, with the other end attached to a lug in the wheel well on the inner side, you can see what happens here: attach one end and the other pops off, and vice versa. I nearly lost my temper here, but

a bit of Revell Contacta cement made them sticky enough to hold in place during the whole process. The nose wheel oleo is much the same, as the locating lugs on the base of the leg don't seem to want to make positive contact inside the well, so best to use Contacta again and position the leg, ensuring the lug on the back goes into the hole in the rear bulkhead and then, once all is aligned, add a

dab of cyanoacrylate with a pin to the lugs in the bay to get it all nice and rigid. I had drilled the hole for the pitot slightly bigger earlier, which was just as well as the kit part is more oval than round and I had to reshape the end before it would fit into the hole in the wing. The tip is painted with the buff-able 'Copper' from Gunze-Sangyo, which works very well, although I think I will go with 'Bronze' in future, as it's too bright. Fitting the armoured glass to the inside of the windscreen is tense, but by using tweezers to hold them together, then adding a drop of cyanoacrylate to the inner/lower edge of the tab that projects down into the nose later, you should not have any problems. I had edged my unit in black with a permanent marker, although I don't know if it had a seal? Fitting the upper decking inside the sliding canopy was also a bit testing, I found it best to add a spot of Contacta in the slot in the rear of the canopy (E03), then position the decking. Once it was in situ, run some Gator Glue (thin version) along the edges from the underside, be sparing though, as you do not want capillary action to draw it up into the rest of the canopy. The windscreen could then be attached with cyanoacrylate only on the front tab, because once pressed down there is no need for any more cement and why risk it! The rear section was attached with the thicker version of Gator Glue and that was it, done...

Conclusion

A superb kit, I made a few hash-ups here and there, but that is modelling. I certainly enjoyed making this one and have another in the wings waiting to be built as I learnt a lot from this first one.

Highly recommended to all, without any reservations.

All model photos ©Richard A. Franks 2015

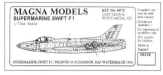

Appendix i

Supermarine Swift Kits, Accessories & Decals

The lists below are as comprehensive as possible, but if there are amendments or additions, please contact the author via the Valiant Wings Publishing address shown at the front of this title. All kits are injection moulded plastic unless otherwise noted.

Kits

1/144th

- Airspede Models [res] Swift F Mk 1#N/K (1999->) - In the 'Basic range'
- Welsh Models [res] 1/144th Swift F.4/FR.5 #PJW17 (1987->)

1/72nd

- Airfix 1/72nd Swift FR.5 #A04003 (2015)
- Britavia Models [vac] Supermarine Swift #N/K - Planned in the mid-1980s but never produced
- CMR [Czech Master Resin] (ex-Czechmaster) [res] Swift FR.5 #135 (2004) - Revised item number to #CMR72-135 with Mark I Ltd's purchase of the brand in 2012
- Czechmaster [res] Swift FR.5 #075* (1995) – This is a generic brand name used to describe the various cottage industry resin kit manufacturers in

Notes

ltd inj	– Limited-run Injection Moulded Plastic
ma	– Self-adhesive tape masks
mtl	– White-metal (including Pewter)
pe	– Photo-etched metal
res	– Resin
vac	– Vacuum-formed Plastic
vma	– Vinyl self-adhesive paint masks
(1999)	– Denotes date the kit was released
(1994->)	– Date/s denote start/finish of firm's activities, the exact date of release of this kit is however unknown
ex-	– Denotes the tooling originated with another firm, the original tool maker is noted after the '-'

CZ at this time * Item number was probably only added by UK importer for reference

- Formaplane [vac] 1/72nd Supermarine Swift #N/K - Release not confirmed
- Hawk Supermarine Swift K-4 #607 (1954) - Also as #607-50 & 607-60
- Magna Models [res/mtl/vac] Swift F Mk 1 #4872 (1997)
- Magna Models [res/mtl/vac] 1/72nd Swift FR Mk 5 #4372 (1997)
- Magna Models [res/mtl/vac] 1/72nd Swift F Mk 7 with Fireflash #4572 (1997)
- Magna Models [res] Swift F Mk 2 #5172 (1998) - Included optional afterburner jet pipe for the record-breaking version
- Merlin Models Swift FR.5 #2 (1984) - Ceased production in 1999
- Pegasus Swift FR.5 #Kit No.22 (1987)
- Project X [vac/mtl] 1/72nd Supermarine 510 #PX 006 (1990)
- Project X [vac/mtl] 1/72nd Supermarine 525 #PX-025 (1993)
- Rareplane [vac] Supermarine Swift FR.5 #N/K (1986) - All moulds sold to Hannants in 1988 - Reissued under Hannants' ownership in 1990s as RP4003
- Testors (ex-Hawk) Supermarine Swift #943 (1995)
- Whirlykits (ex-Project X) [vac/mtl] 1/72nd Supermarine 510 #WPX72012 (1990)
- Xtrakit [ltd inj/res] Supermarine Swift FR.5 #XK72012 (2010)

1/48th

- Contrail [vac] Supermarine Swift #N/K (1989 £5.00)
- Falcon [vac] Supermarine Swift FR.5/F.7 #FV006 (1988) - Reissued in 2004 with metal parts, but no decals
- Formaplane [vac] 1/48th Supermarine Swift #N/K (1986)

Accessories & Masks

- Aeroclub [mtl] 1/72nd Undercarriage Set #V066
- Airkit Enterprises [res/mtl] 1/72nd Supermarine Swift F Mk 1/2 Detail Set {Hawk/Testors}
- Eduard [pe/ma] Swift FR Mk 5 'Big ED' Detail Sets #BIG72105 {Airfix}
- Eduard [pe] Swift FR Mk 5 Detail Set #73-533 {Airfix}
- Eduard [ma] Swift FR.5 Canopy & Wheel masks #CX424 {Airfix}
- Eduard [pe] Swift FR.5 Interior Detail Set - Zoom #SS533 {Airfix}
- Flightpath [pe] Swift Access Ladder #72158
- Freightdog Models [res] Supermarine Swift belly tank #FD72089 {Airfix}
- Freightdog Models [res] Supermarine Swift F Mk 7 Conversion #TBA {Airfix}
- Mark I Models [vac] Supermarine Swift FR Mk 5 Canopy (x2) #MKA7209 {Airfix}
- Pavla Models [res] Supermarine Swift FR Mk 5 Cockpit Detail Set #C72130 {Airfix}
- Pavla Models [res] Martin-Baker Mk 2G Ejection Seat for Swift #S72092 {Airfix}
- Pavla Models [res] Supermarine Swift FR Mk 5 FOD Guards #U72167 {Airfix}

Decals

- Xtradecals 1/72nd RAF No.2 Squadron History 1920-2002 #X72-150
  Includes: Supermarine Swift FR Mk 5 XD962/L, RAF Jever, 1960

Squadrons

What follows is a list of all those squadrons that operated the Supermarine Swift, as well as any other units that used the type.

RAF Squadrons

No.2 (Army Co-operation) Squadron
First operated Swift: 23/02/56
Foreign Bases: Geilenkirchen & Jever
Variants Operated: FR Mk 5
Re-equipped: 13/04/61

No.4 Squadron
First operated Swift: 01/01/61
Foreign Bases: Jever
Variants Operated: FR Mk 5
Re-equipped: 03/61

No.56 (F) Squadron
First operated Swift: (F Mk 1) 20/02/54,
(F Mk 2) 08/54
UK Land Bases: Waterbeach
Variants Operated: F Mks 1 & 2
Re-equipped: 15/03/55

No.79 Squadron
First operated Swift: 14/06/56
Foreign Bases: Wunstorf & Gütersloh
Variants Operated: FR Mk 5
Re-equipped: 30/12/60

F Mk 4 WK275 seen at Hatfield for trials in the 1960s (©via Jet Art Aviation Ltd)

Other Units that used The Swift

Royal Air Force – Other
Air Fighting Development Squadron (AFDS) of the Central Flying School (CFE), RAF West Raynham
WK205, WK206, WK211, WK212, WK216, WK253, XD911 & XD918

No.1 Guided Weapons Development Squadron, RAF Valley
Operated ten of the twelve F Mk 7s built for trials of the Fairey Blue Sky (later Fireflash) beam-riding air-to-air missile.
XF115, XF116, XF117, XF118, XF119, XF120, XF121, XF122, XF123 & XF124

Government & Research
A&AEE, Boscombe Down
The below-listed Swifts were at some stage operating from Boscombe Down, although in some instances this may have been for as little as a single day
VV106, VV119, WJ965, WK194, WK185, WK196, WK197, WK200, WK201, WK202, WK214, WK216, WK219, WK220, WK241, WK244, WK248, WK253, WK272, WK275, WK279, WK291, WK294, XD903, XD904, XD905, XD907, XF113, XF114, XF774, XF780

Empire Test Pilot's School (ETPS), Farnborough
XF113

RAE Farnborough & Bedford
WK199, WK215, WK247, XF774

Rolls-Royce Ltd
WK203 – Used in relation to research into engine surge problems

de Havilland Aircraft Ltd, Hatfield
WK204, WK275

F Mk 4 WK198 fuselage at Farnborough 1998

(©Author's collection)

A colour shot of No.79 Squadron FR Mk 5 WK303
(©Air Ministry)

An unidentified Swift F Mk 7 seen during Fireflash trials with No.1 GWDS (©Author's collection)

Bibliography

This list of Supermarine Swift related publications is as comprehensive as possible, but there are bound to be omissions so if you have amendments or additions, please contact the author via the Valiant Wings Publishing address shown at the front of this title.

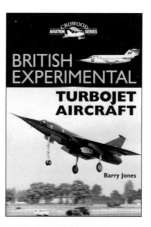
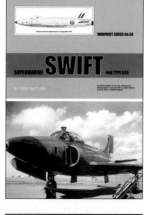
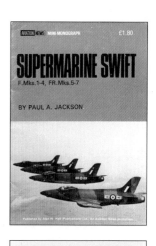

Official Documents
- Swift F Mk 1 - Air Publication 4348A
- Swift F Mk 2 - Air Publication 4348B
- Swift F Mk 3 - Air Publication 4348C
- Swift F Mk 4 - Air Publication 4348D
- Swift FR Mk 5 - Air Publication 4348E
- Swift PR Mk 6 - Air Publication 4348F (Never issued)
- Swift FR Mk 7 - Air Publication 4348G

Publications
- Aircraft Archive - Post War Jets Volume 3 [Type 541] (Argus Books 1988 ISBN:0-85242-967-3)
- British Secret Projects - Jet Fighters since 1950 by Tony Buttler (Midland Publishing 2000 ISBN: 1-85780-095-8)
- Coronation Wings - The Men & Machines of the Royal Air Force Coronation Review at Odiham 15 July 1953 by E. Bucklow (Hikoki Publications 1998 ISBN: 0-951899-6-0)
- RAF Jet Fighter Flypast (Ian Allan)
- Supermarine Aircraft since 1914 by C.F. Andrews & E.B. Morgan (Putnam 1981 ISBN: 0-370-10018-2)
- Supermarine Swift F Mks 1-4, FR Mks 5-7 by Paul A. Jackson, Aviation News Mini-Monograph (Alan W. Hall (Publications) Ltd, 1981)
- Supermarine Swift and Type 535 by T. Buttler, Warpaint Series No.58 (Warpaint Books Ltd)
- Supermarine Attacker, Swift and Scimitar by P. Birtles, Postwar Military Aircraft No.7 (Ian Allan

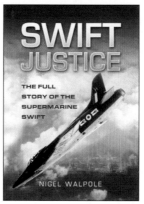

Ltd 1992 ISBN: 0-7110-2034-5)
- Spitfire - A Test Pilot's Story by Jeffrey Quill OBE, AFC, FRAeS (Arrow Books 1983 & 1989 ISBN: 0-09-937020-4)
- Swift Justice: The Full Story of the Supermarine Swift by N. Walpole (Pen & Sword Books 2004 ISBN: 1-84415-070-4)
- The British Fighter since 1912 by Francis K. Mason (Putnam ISBN: 0-85177-852-6)
- The Cold War Years: Flight Testing at Boscombe Down 1945-1975 by T. Mason (Hikoki Publications 2001 ISBN: 1-902109-11-2)

Periodicals & Part-works
- Aeroplane Monthly, March 1977
- Aviation News Vol.11 No.11
- Scale Aviation Modeller International Vol.4 Iss.4 April 1998

Supermarine Swift adv (colour) 1953

Swift FR5 Fiji stamp

Type 541 cigarette card

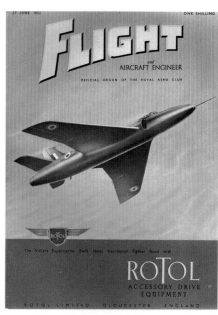

Flight 27-06-52